5th EDITION

NEW COMPLETE GEOGRAPHY SKILLS BOOK

CHARLES HAYES

Gill Education
Hume Avenue
Park West
Dublin 12
www.gilleducation.ie

Gill Education is an imprint of M.H. Gill & Co.

978 07171 6519 3

Design and print origination by Design Image

The paper used in this book is made from the wood pulp of managed forests. For every tree felled, at least one tree is planted, thereby renewing natural resources.

Any links to external websites should not be construed as an endorsement by Gill Education of the content or view of the linked material. Furthermore it cannot be guaranteed that all external links will be live.

For permission to reproduce photographs, the author and publisher gratefully acknowledge the following:
© Alamy: 3R, 9TL, 10R, 12BR, 14, 21CL, 28TR, 28BL, 28BR, 49, 115BL, 116CB, 120L, 120R, 121T, 121CT, 135T, 135B, 171, 178C, chapter headers 21–24, chapter headers 31-34, chapter headers 59–64; © Bord na Mona: 140C, 140B; © Brian Solomon: 140T; © Brick: 126, 166; © Digital Globe/OSI: 75; © Fairtrade: 178B; © FLPA: 21T; © Getty Images: 12BL, 16T, 16C, 116CT; © Imagefile: 28TL; © Martyn Turner: 172; © NASA/GSFC/JPL: 21BR; © Peter Barrow: 71; © Polyp: 177; © Press Association: 16B; © Science Photo Library: 9TR, 9BL; © Shutterstock: 3L, 8, 9BC, 9BR, 10L, 13, 24, 34, 51TL, 51TC, 51TR, 115BC, 115BR, 116T, 116B, 120C, 121C, 121CB, 121B, 135C, chapter headers 1–7, chapter headers 8–19, chapter header 20, chapter headers 25–30, chapter headers 35–42, chapter headers 43–58; © Shutterstock/trekandshoot: 119

The author and publisher have made every effort to trace all copyright holders, but if any has been inadvertently overlooked we would be pleased to make the necessary arrangement at the first opportunity.

Ordnance Survey Ireland Permit No. 9000
© Ordnance Survey Ireland/Government of Ireland

Contents

Introduction

New Complete Geography Skills Book is the perfect companion to *New Complete Geography* textbook. It provides an ideal activity book and exam-trainer that can be used in class or for homework.

- The Skills book tracks the Junior Certificate **syllabus** and *New Complete Geography* textbook chapter by chapter.

- It contains a comprehensive selection of past Junior Certificate examination questions. It also trains students to **maximise** their **examination performances** by the repeated use of easy-to-correct examination questions, marking schemes and sample answers.

- It fosters literacy, numeracy and other **skills** by the active and imaginative use of news extracts, pictures, statistics, maps, graphs, charts, cartoons and other media.

- It includes a wide range of **games and fun activities** that are designed to promote active learning, to enhance skills and to reinforce knowledge.

- It is Ireland's **market leading** and **most comprehensive** Skills Book or Workbook.

New Complete Geography has already helped countless students in Ireland to understand, engage with and enjoy Geography. This completely updated edition of the *New Complete Geography Skills Book* will continue to help students reach their maximum potential through active, enjoyable and effective learning. We hope you enjoy it!

Charles Hayes

Layers of the Earth

1 In the spaces provided in Figure 1, name each layer of the earth labelled **A, B, C** and **D**.

2 In relation to Figure 1, indicate whether each of the following statements is true or false (circle the correct *True / False* alternative in each case):

(a) The hottest part of the earth is at **B**. *True / False*

(b) **A** consists of plates which collide with and separate from each other. *True / False*

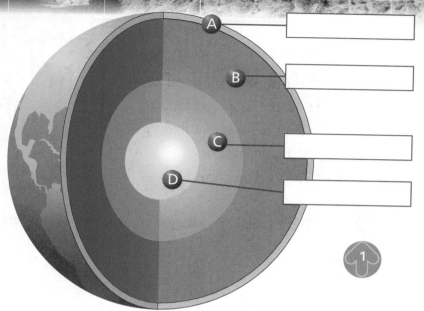

Crustal Plates

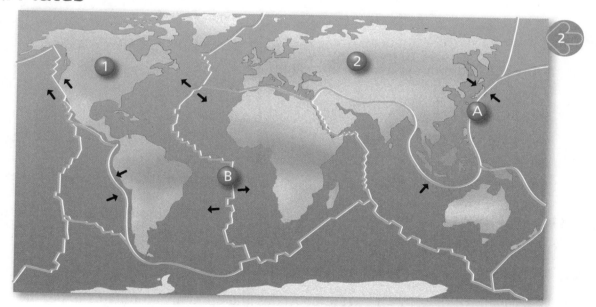

3 Examine the map in Figure 2, which shows some of the world's principal crustal plates.

(a) Name the crustal plates labelled **1** and **2**.

1 _____ 2 _____

(b) Circle the correct option in **each** of the statements below.

(i) The area at **A** is a major earthquake zone. *True / False*

(ii) The area at **B** is known as the Mid-Atlantic Ridge. *True / False*

Folding

4 (a) Feature **X** in Figure 3 is:

A mid-ocean ridge ☐

A fold mountain ☐

The mantle ☐

(b) Feature **X** was formed by:

Compression and faulting ☐

Compression and folding ☐

Plates separating ☐

Tick (✓) the correct box.

Plate 1   Plate 2

3

5 (a) With the aid of a diagram, explain how fold mountains are formed.

_____

_____

_____

_____

_____

_____

(b) Name one fold mountain range in Ireland.

_____

Diagram of feature

6 Photographs **A** and **B** on the page opposite show parts of two different fold mountain ranges: the Andes in South America and the Galty Mountains in Munster.

(a) Which mountains are shown in photograph **A**? _____

(b) Describe the differences between the Andes and the Galty Mountains under the headings given below.

	Andes	Galty Mountains
Height		
Age		
Foldings in which they originated		

Earthquakes

7 Cross out the **incorrect word** in each of the statements.

Strong earthquakes happen in *Ireland / California.*

Mid-ocean ridges are formed when plates are in *collision / separation.*

Fold mountains are formed when plates are in *collision / separation.*

8 In the spaces provided name each of the things described or indicated in (a) to (d) below:

(a) An instrument used to measure the strength of earthquakes.

_____

(b) The scale used to record the strength of earthquakes.

_____

(c) A destructive tidal wave that may result from an under-seabed earthquake.

_____

(d) The features indicated by:

  ● Label **X** in Figure 4: _____

  ● Label **Y** in Figure 4: _____

  ● Label **Z** in Figure 4: _____

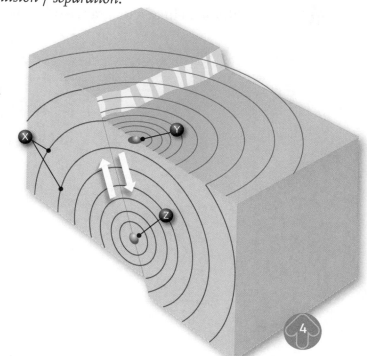

9 With the aid of a diagram, explain how an earthquake occurs.

Terms (not given in order) that should be included in this answer:
– Plate movements – Seismic (shock) waves – Epicentre – Rocks crack – Surface tremors – Focus

Diagram

10 (a) With the help of a diagram explain what a tsunami is.

Diagram

(b) Describe one effect of a tsunami hitting a large city.

11 Test your judgement:

Imagine that you are caught in a sudden, violent earthquake. **What would you do while the tremor lasts?** Five of the suggestions given below are correct. The rest are not. Tick the box after each of the suggestions that you think is correct. Then check your answer against the solutions on page 7.

If in your classroom:

(a) Move close to a window ☐

(b) Get out immediately and take the lift downstairs ☐

(c) Get out immediately and run to the playground ☐

(d) Cover your head and neck ☐

(e) Remain sitting at your desk and hold on to it ☐

(f) Get under your desk and hold on to it ☐

If out of doors:

(g) Scream for help ☐

(h) Get into the open, away from all buildings ☐

(i) Hide under the nearest tree ☐

(j) Run away from the epicentre of the earthquake ☐

(k) Use your smartphone to take photographs ☐

(l) Carefully walk to a house and shelter under the doorway ☐

(m) Take shelter under a nearby cliff ☐

If driving:

(n) Stop your car suddenly and run ☐

(o) Stay inside your car ☐

(p) Drive out of the area as quickly as possible ☐

(q) Drive under a bridge and stop ☐

(r) Text your local Garda station for advice ☐

(s) Stop your car carefully as far out of traffic as possible ☐

12 Name the features of a volcano that are labelled **A**, **B**, **C**, **D** and **E** on Figure 5.

A   _____

B   _____

C   _____

D   _____

E   _____

13 The map shows some crustal plates and their boundaries.

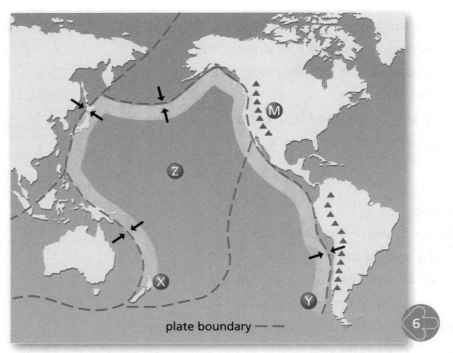

plate boundary — —

Circle the correct answer in **each** of the statements below:

(a) The shaded area labelled **X–Y** is *the Pacific Ring of Fire / the Great Pacific Ridge*.

(b) The plate labelled **Z** is *the Nazca Plate / the Pacific Plate / the American Plate*.

(c) The mountains labelled **M** are called *the Andes / the Rockies / the Himalayas*.

(d) The shaded area is so called because it contains many *volcanoes / forest fires*.

(e) The map shows that crustal plates *collide / separate* along much of the shaded area.

14 Funtime

Clues Across

1. South American fold mountains.
3. On top of a volcanic mountain.
6. Comes out of volcanoes.
8. African country and mountain.
10. Inside the earth but sounds like a cover.
11. Volcanic material or soil and water.
13. Outer part of bread or earth.
14. American city prone to earthquakes.
15. Pipe through which volcano erupts.
18. Volcanic Pacific island, 20°N, 156°W.
19. Cazan – a mixed-up plate.
21. This volcanic country sounds really cool.
22. County/city in Northern Ireland.
23. Crustal plate 'down under'.

Clues Down

1. Volcanic material or burnt-out fuel wood.
2. You cannot eat from these pieces of earth-crust.
3. The planet's centre.
4. Sicilian volcano that sounds like a girl's name.
5. Physical features (L A _ D _ O R M S).
7. When the ground trembles.
9. Ireland's crustal plate.
12. Was 6 across before it flows out of a vent.
16. A dead volcano, e.g. Slemish.
17. Beneath the Mid Atlantic.
20. Around the Pacific – a 'Ring of _ _ _ _'.

Solutions to Activity 11 from page 5. The correct suggestions are (d), (f), (h), (o), (s)

1 Which of the following types of rock is shown in Figure 1?

metamorphic ☐

igneous ☐

sedimentary ☐

Tick (✓) the correct box.

2 Write in the boxes the type of rock (limestone, sandstone, etc.) that is most likely to be found in each of the locations labelled 1–5 on the map in Figure 2.

1	
2	
3	
4	
5	

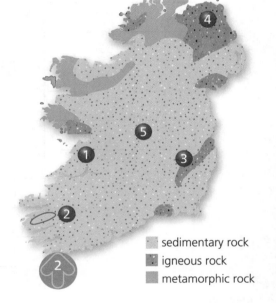

sedimentary rock
igneous rock
metamorphic rock

3 Choose **three** terms from the *selection box* to fill in the spaces in the *extract* below.

Selection Box

Metamorphic   Sandstone   Basalt
Quartzite   Shale   Igneous
Marble   Sedimentary   Limestone

Extract

'There are many types of rock in Ireland. These range from regular-shaped columns of _____
in Antrim's Giant's Causeway to multi-coloured granite on the Wicklow Mountains. Both of these rock types are

_____, which means they were once formed from hot, volcanic material. The centre of Ireland

consists mostly of _____, in which fossils of ancient sea creatures can sometimes be found.'

4 Examine each of the rocks in the pictures labelled **A–E**. In the grid provided state the name and rock group, along with a possible use and pominent location of each rock. One of the rocks is not studied in chapter 2 of your textbook Research the information about it online.

This rock was once limestone

A grainy rock

Ireland's most common rock

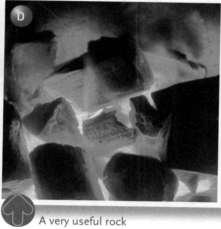
A very useful rock

Rock with visible crystals that formed inside the earth's surface

	Name of rock	Rock group	Possible use	Prominent location
A				
B				
C				
D				
E				

5 Examine **Picture A** and **Picture B**, which show two different rock types in Ireland. Answer the questions that follow.

The Giant's Causeway

The Burren, Co. Clare

(a) Name the type of rock shown in:

Picture A _____

Picture B _____

(b) Indicate whether each rock type you named is igneous, sedimentary or metamorphic.

Picture A _____

Picture B _____

(c) Describe two ways in which rocks may be of benefit to people.

(i) _____

(ii) _____

6 In the boxes provided, match each letter in Column X with the number of its pair in Column Y. One match has been completed for you.

COLUMN X	
A	Ireland's most common sedimentary rock
B	Metamorphic rock that was once sandstone
C	Igneous rock found at the Giant's Causeway, Co. Antrim
D	Coarse multi-coloured igneous rock found in Wicklow
E	A fossil fuel found in the Midlands of Ireland

COLUMN Y	
1	Quartzite
2	Granite
3	Limestone
4	Basalt
5	Peat

A	3
B	
C	
D	
E	

7 Which of the following are **all examples of sedimentary rocks?** *Tick (✓) the correct box.*

(a) Granite, limestone and quartzite ☐

(b) Granite, marble and quartzite ☐

(c) Marble, coal and sandstone ☐

(d) Sandstone, limestone and shale ☐

8 Imagine a quarry is to be opened near where you live. Explain why some people would be in favour of it **and** why some people would be against it.

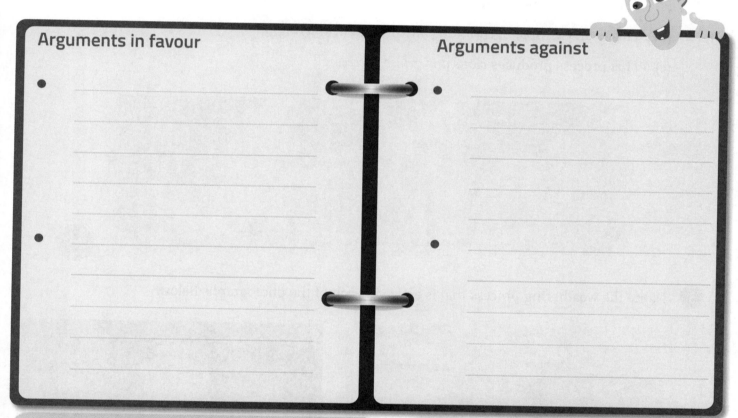

Arguments in favour

Arguments against

Marking scheme

Use the following marking scheme to judge your performance in ansering the question above.
- The entire question is allocated **12 marks**.
- Your can score **3 marks for each argument** (there must be two arguments in favour and two arguments against the quarry).
- Each argument should be marked as follows:
  - Allow **2 marks** for *making* a clear argument/point.
  - Allow **1 mark** for *developing* the argument.

Example:

The quarry might produce air²✓ pollution in the form of dust. This might damage the health of local people or quarry workers who inhale the dust.⁺¹✓

3/3

1 Weathering of rock is caused by:

rivers ☐

climatic change ☐

freezing and thawing ☐

volcanic activity ☐

2 **Circle** the correct answer in **each** of the statements below.

(a) The process shown in figure 1 is *freeze-thaw action / solution*.

(b) This is an example of *chemical / mechanical weathering*.

(c) This process produces *clints and grikes / scree*.

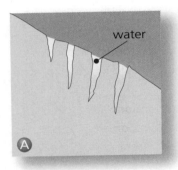

water

A

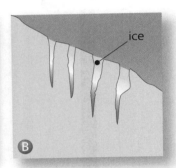

ice

B

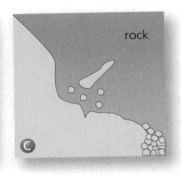

rock

C

3 Name the **weathering process** that is active in each of the photographs below.

4 With the aid of a labelled diagram(s), explain how frost action occurs.

(10 marks)

_____

_____

_____

_____

_____

_____

Diagram(s)

5 (a) The broken-down rock found in this upland area, Croagh Patrick, has resulted from:

Tick (✓) the correct box.

Solution ☐

Mechanical weathering ☐

Carbonation ☐

(b) What name is given to this broken-down rock?

_____

6 The photograph shows limestone that has been weathered.

Circle the correct **option** in each of the statements below:

(a) This rock is *sandstone / limestone*.

(b) This feature is formed by *chemical weathering / mechanical weathering*.

(c) An example of this feature can be found in the *Burren, Co. Clare / Giant's Causeway, Co. Antrim*.

7 (a) Name the category of rock in which limestone belongs. _____

(b) Name a location where limestone is found. _____

(c) Describe fully how the rock shown in the photograph in Question 6 is weathered by rainwater.

_____

_____

_____

_____

_____

_____

8 In the boxes provided, match each letter in Column X with the number of its pair in Column Y.

COLUMN X		COLUMN Y				
A	Stalagmite	1	Deep cracks in the limestone pavement		A	
B	Clints	2	Deposits of calcite hanging from the roof of a cave		B	
C	Stalactite	3	Blocks of limestone		C	
D	Grikes	4	Deposits of calcite on the floor of a cave		D	1

9 In the grid provided, write the names of each of the features laelled **A–I** in Figure 2.

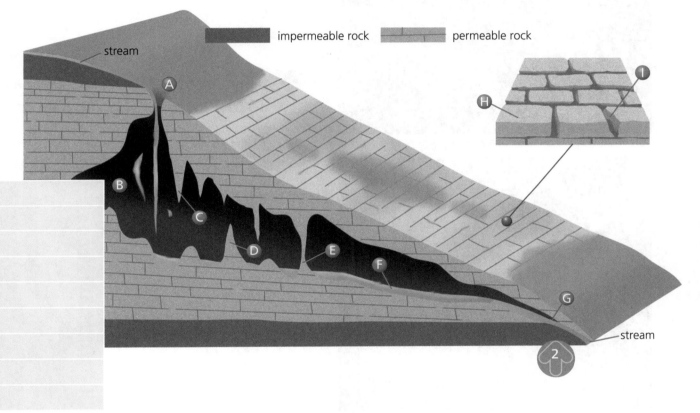

A	
B	
C	
D	
E	
F	
G	
H	
I	

10 Many tourists visit the wide range of attractions in the Burren. While these tourists bring many *benefits* to the area, they also cause some *problems*. In the spaces below, describe two benefits and two problems of tourism for the Burren.

Benefits	Problems
•	•
•	•

1 Identify the type of mass movement that is shown in each of the pictures **A**, **B** and **C**.

A _____

B _____

C _____

2 Name one type of slow mass movement and describe its effects.

Type: _____

_____

Effects: _____

_____

_____

_____

_____

_____

_____

_____

_____

_____

_____

_____

_____

_____

_____

_____

Chapter 4

③ Mass Movement

The diagrams show a type of mass movement.

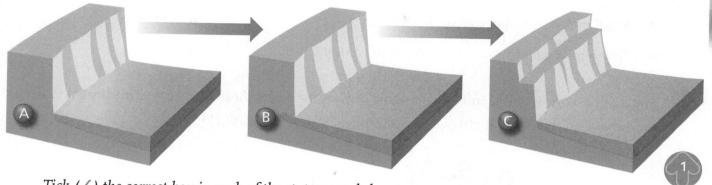

Tick (✓) the correct box in each of the statements below.

(a) The process shown is:

soil creep ☐   a landslide ☐

(b) The type of mass movement shown is:

rapid ☐   slow ☐

(c) The type of mass movement shown is most likely to occur:

at the side of a calm lake ☐   on a stormy coast ☐

④ Try to explain each of the following:

● How precipitation and gradient influences mass movement.

_____

_____

_____

● How vegetation might help to prevent mass movement.

_____

_____

_____

● How an earthquake might cause a landslide to happen.

_____

_____

_____

5 Circle the correct **option** in each of the statements below.

(a) Mudflows are one of the fastest forms of mass movement. *True / False*

(b) Mudflows occur in dry areas. *True / False*

(c) Gradient is very important for mass movement. *True / False*

6 The diagrams **A**, **B** and **C** in Figure 2 show how human activities could have contributed to mass movement on the Dart line between Greystones and Bray, Co. Wicklow.

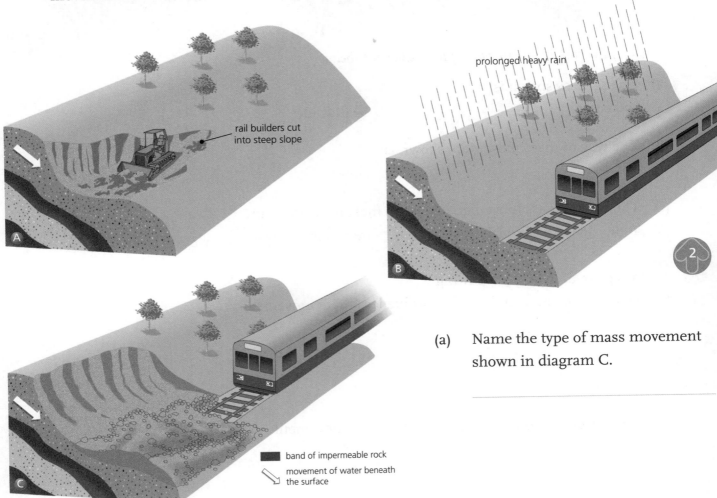

rail builders cut into steep slope

prolonged heavy rain

band of impermeable rock

movement of water beneath the surface

(a) Name the type of mass movement shown in diagram C.

_____

(b) With the help of the three diagrams, attempt to explain why this mass movement happened.

_____

_____

_____

_____

1 The diagrams **A**, **B** and **C** show a river in its upper, middle and lower courses.

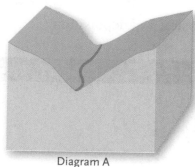

Diagram A

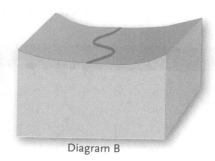

Diagram B

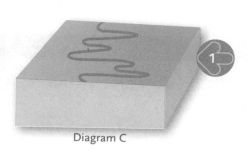

Diagram C

Circle the correct answer in **each** of the statements below:

(a) Sideward erosion is most common in *Diagram A / Diagram B / Diagram C.*

(b) Deposition is most common in *Diagram A / Diagram B / Diagram C.*

(c) Downward erosion is most common in *Diagram A / Diagram B / Diagram C.*

2 (a) Look at Figure 2, which shows part of the course of a river. The **feature** maked Z is called:

a waterfall ☐

a delta ☐

an estuary ☐

a meander ☐

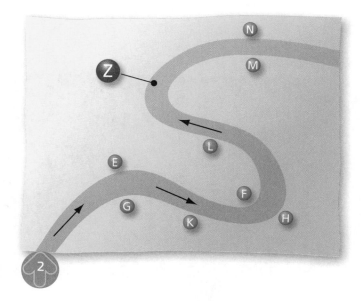

(b) The river is:

eroding at A and depositing at B ☐

eroding at C and depositing at D ☐

eroding at E and depositing at F ☐

eroding at G and depositing at H ☐

Tick (✓) the correct box.

3 Recognise river features

- In *Column 1* of the grid provided write the names of the river features that are labelled *A–M* on the illustrations that appear on this page and the next page.
- In *Column 2* indicate whether each of the features shown is more likely to be found in the *upper* or the *lower* course of a river.
- In *Column 3* indicate whether each feature is the result of river *erosion* or river *deposition*. You may omit features D, E, H, I and J (which are created by erosion *and* depoisition).

	Column 1	Column 2	Column 3
A			
B			
C			
D			
E			
F			
G			
H			
I			
J			
K			
L			
M			

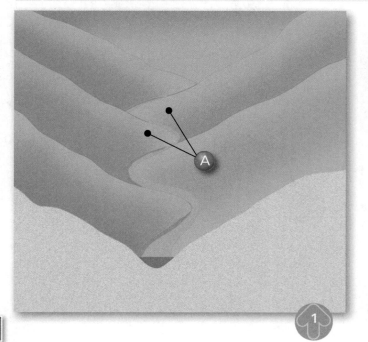

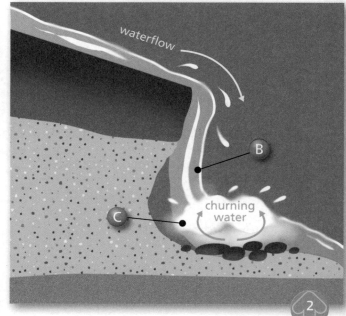

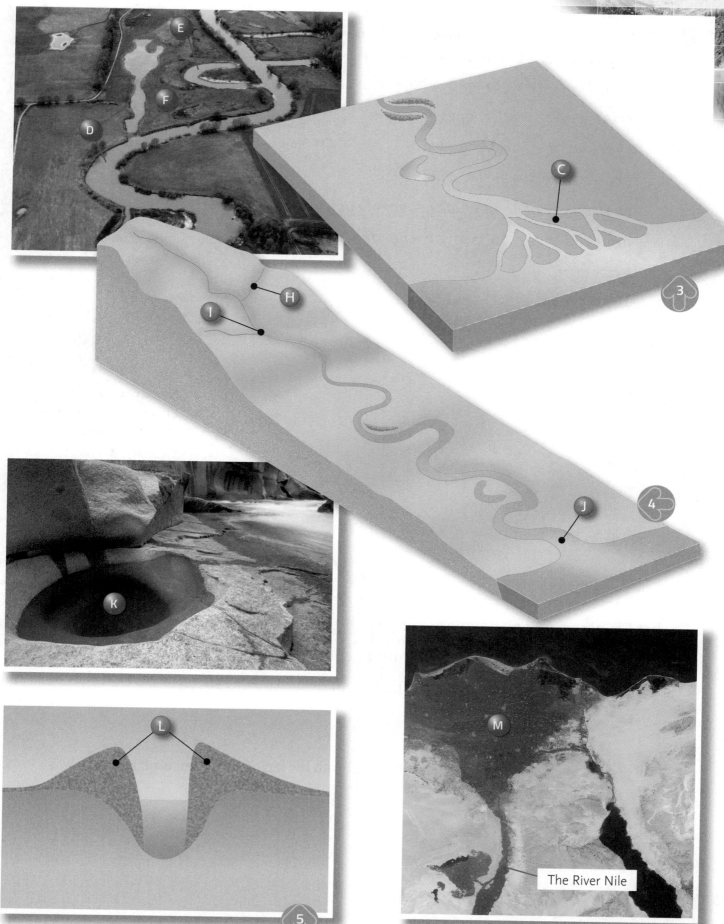

The River Nile

4 (a) Name **one** feature of river erosion and with the aid of a diagram explain how it was formed. *(10)*

A waterfall is formed when a   **2** ✓
river erodes soft rock faster   **2** ✓
than hard rock. A vertical
drop then develops where
the hard rock meets the soft rock   **1** ✓
and the river falls over the drop as a
waterfall.

This is a corrected sample answer to question (a)

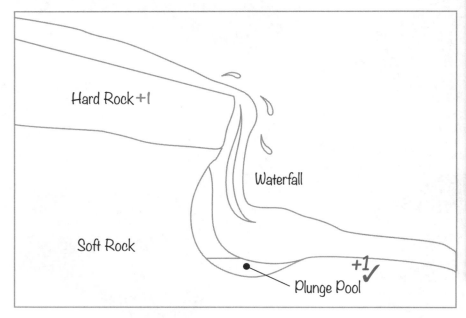

Hard Rock **+1**

Waterfall

Soft Rock

Plunge Pool **+1** ✓

A plunge pool develops at the base of the waterfall. Abrasion and   **2** ✓
hydraulic action in the plunge pool undercuts the waterfall and   **+1** ✓
causes it to be eroded upstream.

(b) Name **one** feature of river deposition and with the aid of a diagram explain how it was formed. *(10)*

Junior Cert Marking Scheme

(a) **10 marks**
- **Name** feature of river erosion: *2 marks*
- Explain how formed: **two explanations** at **4 marks each**. Each *4 marks* given as follows:
  - Clear statement: *2m*
  - One development: *1m*
  - One reference to **diagram** (such as to a label in the diagram): *1m*

(b) **10 marks**
(Similar marking scheme as for (a) above)

(c) **5 marks**
- **Name one use:** *2 marks*
- Brief **explanation**: *3 marks* given as follows:
  - Statement: *2m*
  - One development: *1m*

(d) **5 marks**
(Similar marking scheme as for (c) above)

_____
_____
_____
_____
_____
_____
_____
_____

Diagram of feature

(c)   Name and briefly explain **one** way in which people use rivers. *(5)*

_____
_____
_____
_____
_____
_____
_____

(d)   Name and briefly explain **one** way in which people pollute rivers. *(5)*

_____
_____
_____
_____
_____
_____
_____

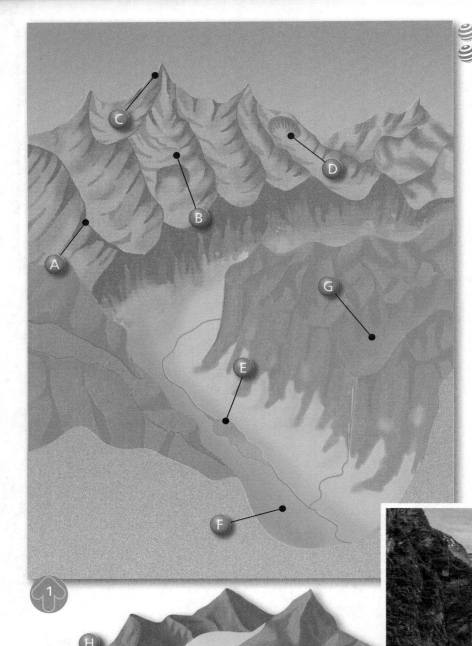

1 **Recognising glacial features.**
Examine the illustrations of glacial landforms that are shown on this page and on the next page.

In *Column 1* of the grid provided write the names of the glacial features that are labelled *A–L*.

In *Column 2* indicate whether each feature is formed by glacial erosion of by glacial deposition.

In *Column 3* indicate whether each feature is more likely to be found in an upland or in a lowland area.

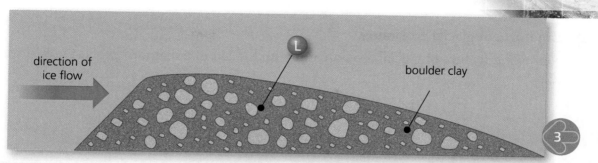

	Column 1	Column 2	Column 3
A			
B			
C			
D			
E			
F			
G			
H			
I			
J			
K			
L			

 2 In the boxes provided, match each letter in Column X with the number of its pair in Column Y. One pair has been completed for you.

	COLUMN X
A	Corrie
B	Arête
C	Fjord
D	Hanging valley
E	Ribbon lake

	COLUMN Y
1	Narrow ridge between two corries
2	Glaciated valley overhanging main valley
3	Hollow on valley floor scooped out by ice
4	Steep-sided hollow sometimes containing a lake
5	Glaciated valley drowned by rising sea levels

A	4
B	
C	
D	
E	

3 (a) **Landform of glacial erosion**

Name one feature of glacial erosion and with the aid of a diagram explain how it was formed. *(10)*

Diagram

(b) **Landform of glacial deposition**

Name one feature of glacial deposition and with the aid of a diagram explain how it was formed. *(10)*

Diagram

(c) Glaciation and people

(i) Name and briefly explain one way in which people benefit from the results of glaciation. *(5)*

(ii) Name and briefly explain one disadvantage of the results of glaciation. *(5)*

Junior Cert Higher Level Marking Scheme for question 3

(a) Landform of glacial erosion

Name feature: *2 marks*

Explain how formed: **two explanations** at *3 marks each* to be allocated as follows:

- Statement: *2m*
- One development: *1m*

Diagram: *2 marks* (*1m* for diagram and 1m for at least one named label)

(b) Landform of glacial deposition

(Same marking scheme as for (a) above)

(c) Glaciation and people

Benefit

Name one benefit: *2 marks*

Explain benefit: *3 marks* allocated as follows:

- Statement: *2m*
- One development *1m*

Disadvantage

(Same marking scheme as for **benefit** above)

4 Which of the following are **all features of glacial erosion**?
Tick (✓) the correct box.

(a) Fjord, moraine, pyramidal peak ☐

(b) Arête, cirque, U-shaped valley ☐

(c) Boulder clay, cirque, hanging valley ☐

(d) Arête, cirque, drumlin ☐

1 **Recognising coastal features**

Examine the features/landforms labelled *A–N* in Figure 1 and on the photographs on this page.

On the grid provided on the next page, name each **feature** and indicate whether it is formed by sea **erosion** or **deposition**. Name also one **Irish example** of each feature. (You may have to research on the internet for some of these examples.)

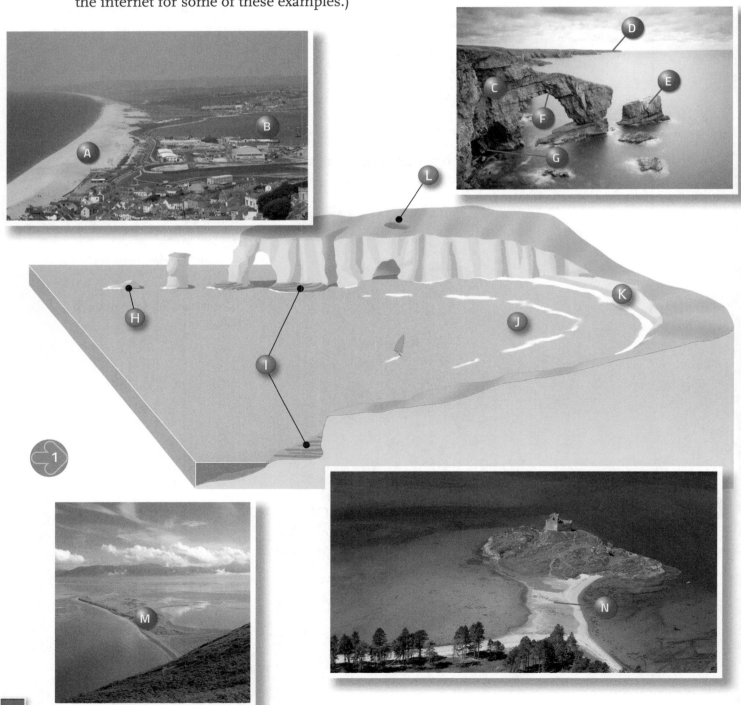

	Name of feature	Erosion or deposition	Irish Example
A			
B			
C			
D			
E			
F			
G			
H			
I			
J			
K			
L			
M			
N			

2 In the boxes provided, match each letter in Column X with the number of its pair in Column Y. One pair has been completed for you.

	COLUMN X
A	Lagoon
B	Abrasion
C	Tombolo
D	Longshore drift
E	Sand dune
F	Storm beach
G	Sand spit

	COLUMN Y
1	Links a former island to the mainland
2	Bay cut off from the sea by a body of sand
3	Mounds of sand anchored by marram grass
4	Ridge of sand and shingle jutting out into the sea
5	Deposition when waves are very strong
6	Movement of material along a beach
7	Erosion by the load carried by waves

A	
B	
C	1
D	
E	
F	
G	

3 **(a) Feature of coastal erosion**

Name one feature of coastal erosion and with the aid of a diagram explain how it was formed. *(10)*

_____

_____

_____

_____

_____

_____

_____

_____

_____

_____

_____

_____

_____

_____

Junior Cert Higher Level Marking Scheme for question 3

(a) Feature of coastal erosion
Name feature: *2 marks*
Explain how formed: **two explanations** at *3 marks each* to be allocated as follows:
● Statement: *2m*
● One development: *1m*

Diagram: *2 marks* (*1m* for diagram and *1m* for at least one named label)

(b) Feature of glacial erosion
(Same marking scheme as for (a) above)

(c) Coasts and people
How people use coastal areas
Name one benefit: *2 marks*
Explain benefit: *3 marks* allocated as follows:
● Statement: *2m*
● One development: *1m*

How people pollute coastal areas
(Same marking scheme as for **coastal areas** above)

Diagram

(b) Feature of glacial erosion

Name one feature of coastal deposition and with the aid of a diagram explain how it was formed. *(10)*

Diagram

(c) Coasts and people

(i)   Name and briefly explain one way in which people use coastal areas. *(5)*

(ii)   Name and briefly explain one way in which people pollute coastal areas. *(5)*

4 **Map reading skills**

Eleven different coastal landforms are labelled 1–11 in **red** on the **Ordnance Survey maps** in Figures 2 and 3. Try to match each label with the matching named landform in the grid below. (One match has been completed for you. Some features have been named and labelled on the map to help you identify some numbered features.)

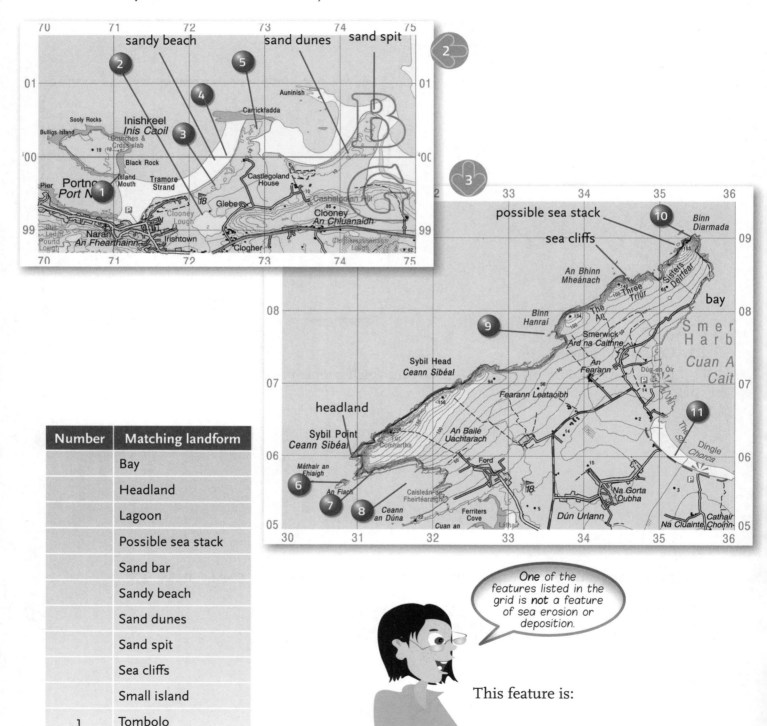

Number	Matching landform
	Bay
	Headland
	Lagoon
	Possible sea stack
	Sand bar
	Sandy beach
	Sand dunes
	Sand spit
	Sea cliffs
	Small island
1	Tombolo

One of the features listed in the grid is **not** a feature of sea erosion or deposition.

This feature is:

_____

1 The diagram in Figure 1 illustrates **global warming**. Complete the diagram by selecting labels from the *selection box* and writing them into the boxes labelled **A–F**.

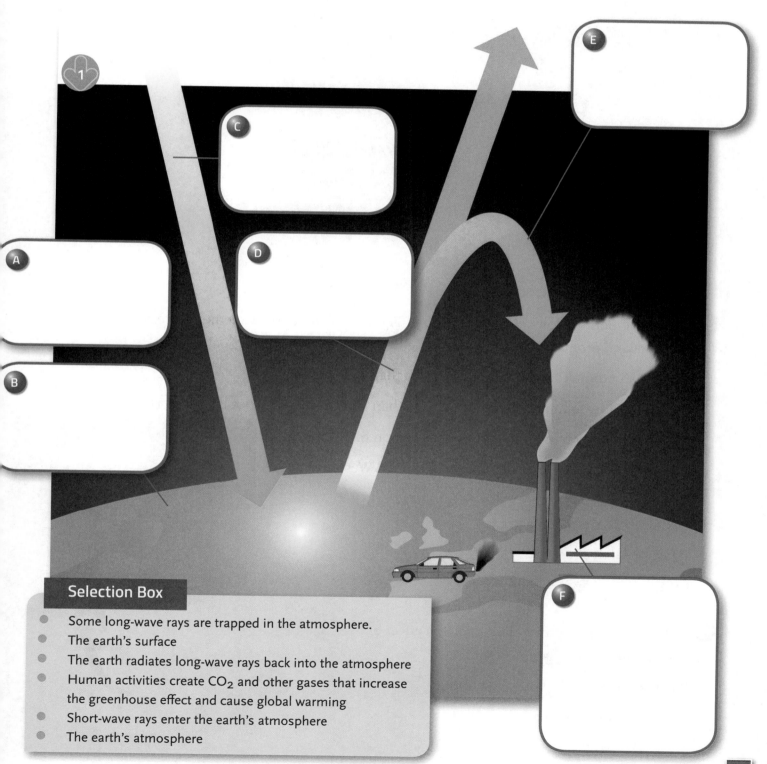

Selection Box

- Some long-wave rays are trapped in the atmosphere.
- The earth's surface
- The earth radiates long-wave rays back into the atmosphere
- Human activities create CO_2 and other gases that increase the greenhouse effect and cause global warming
- Short-wave rays enter the earth's atmosphere
- The earth's atmosphere

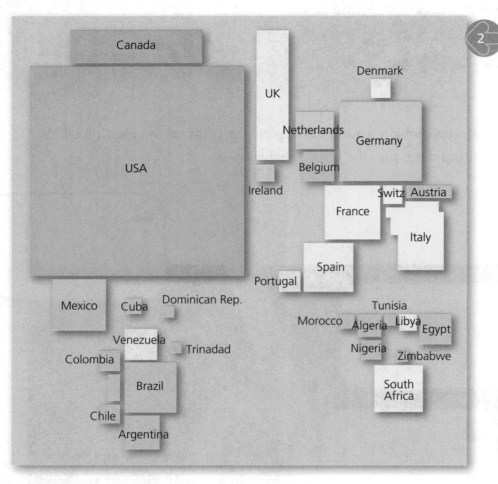

Carbon dioxide (CO_2) emissions in the Americas, Western Europe and Africa

On this map:
- The **sizes** of countries indicate the *total amounts* of CO_2 that they emit.
- The **colours** of countries indicate the average CO_2 *emissions per person* in metric tons in those countries.

	15 and over
	10.0 – 14.9
	5.0 – 9.9
	under 5

2 The statements below refer to the map in Figure 2. *Three* of the statements are correct.

1. Ireland produces more CO_2 than Netherlands.

2. Irish produces more CO_2 per person than Belgium.

3. The USA produces much more CO_2 than all of South America and Africa.

4. Germany produces more CO_2 per person than Canada.

5. North America produces more CO_2 than Western Europe.

The correct statements are:

Tick (✓) the correct box.

1, 2, 3 ☐   2, 3, 4 ☐   2, 3, 5 ☐   3, 4, 5 ☐

3 The cartoon in Figure 3 illustrates the effect of:

Acid rain ☐   Plate tectonics ☐

Weathering ☐   Global warming ☐

Tick (✓) the correct box.

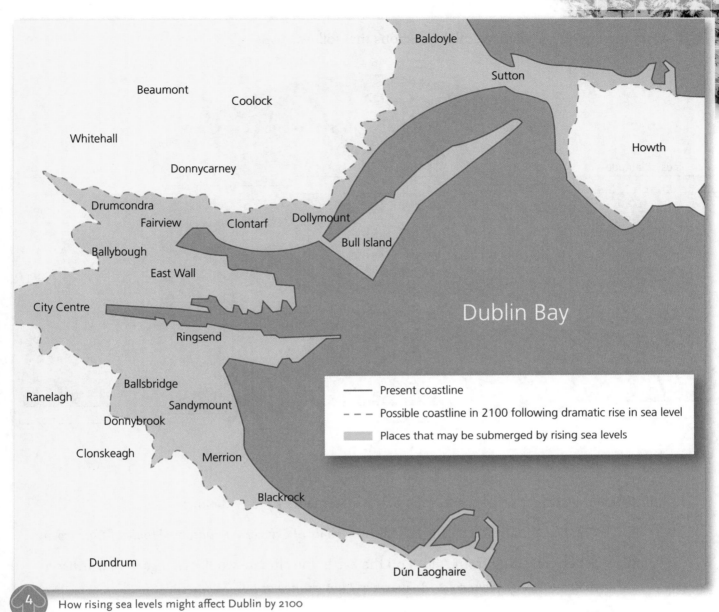

Beaumont
Coolock
Baldoyle
Sutton
Whitehall
Howth
Donnycarney
Drumcondra
Fairview
Clontarf
Dollymount
Ballybough
Bull Island
East Wall
City Centre
Dublin Bay
Ringsend
Ballsbridge
Ranelagh
Sandymount
Donnybrook
Clonskeagh
Merrion
Blackrock
Dundrum
Dún Laoghaire

— Present coastline
- - - Possible coastline in 2100 following dramatic rise in sea level
▨ Places that may be submerged by rising sea levels

4 How rising sea levels might affect Dublin by 2100

4 The map in Figure 4 shows the *possible* effects of severe global warming on Dublin by the year 2100. According to the map, which of the following statements are correct?

A. Ballsbridge, Ringsend and Sutton would all be part of the sea.

B. Coolock, Clonskeagh and Dundrum would all survive the rising sea levels.

C. The north Dublin suburbs of Beaumount, Ranelagh and Donnycarney would all still be part of the land.

D. Dublin Bay would become smaller.

E. Howth would be a new island.

The correct statements are: *Tick (✓) the correct box.*

A, C, E ☐   A, B, E ☐   B, C, D ☐   A, C, D

5 Examine Figure 5 and answer the questions that follow.

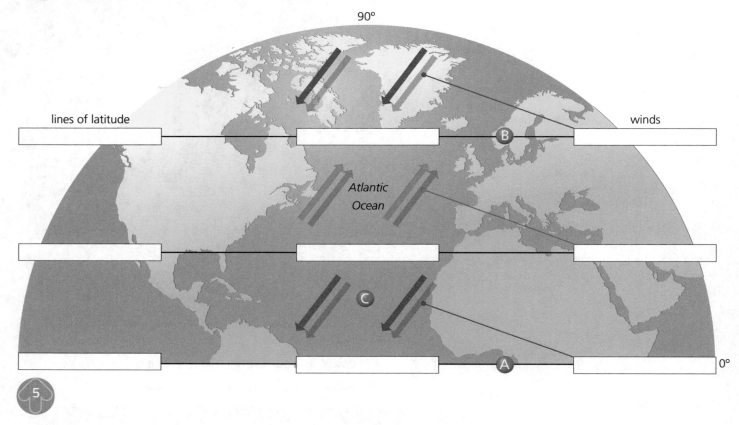

(a) **Circle** the correct response to each of the statements (i) to (v) below:

(i) The line of latitude at **A** is called the: *Tropic of Cancer / Equator / Tropic of Capricorn.*

(ii) When travelling from **A** to **B** on the earth, the climate would: *change from warmer to colder / change from colder to warmer / not change at all.*

(iii) The winds that blow over Ireland are called the: *trade winds / anti-trade winds.*

(iv) The area at **A** is known as the: *doldrums / horse latitudes.*

(v) The winds at **C** tend to *warm / cool* the areas over which they blow.

(b) Complete Figure 4 by filling in the boxes in the diagram.

(i) *The lines of latitude* (in the boxes on the left side).

(ii) *High pressure or low pressure* (in the boxes in the centre).

(iii) *The names of winds* (in the boxes on the right).

6 Ocean currents

(a) Examine the map in Figure 6. Circle the correct answer in each of the statements below.

(i) The current at **X** is a *warm / cold* current.

(ii) The current at **Y** is a *warm / cold* current.

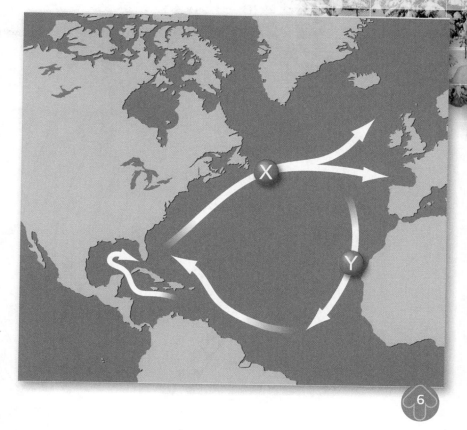

(b) Name the current that is labelled **X**.

_____

(c) Name the current that is labelled **Y**.

_____

(d) The ocean current labelled **X** has several effects on Ireland. Describe **two** of those effects.

● _____
  _____
  _____
  _____
  _____
  _____
  _____

● _____
  _____
  _____
  _____
  _____
  _____
  _____
  _____

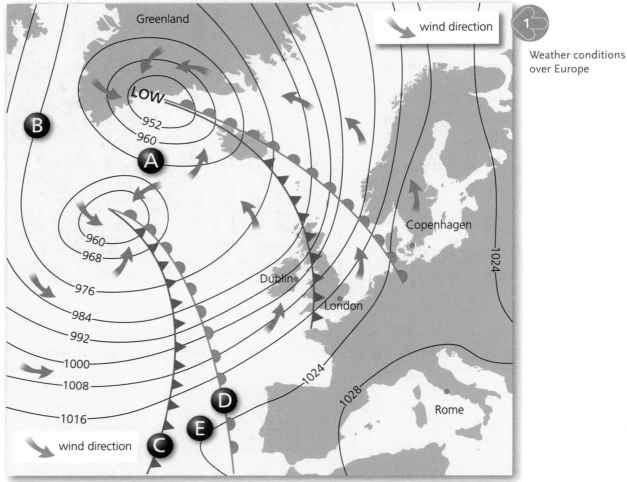

Weather conditions over Europe

1 Examine the weather chart in Figure 1.

   (a) Insert the word HIGH in an appropriate place on the map.

   (b) Insert the word LOW in an appropriate place (but not where 'LOW' is already written).

   (c) Name the weather system that is centred close to the south of Greenland.

   (d) The missing number at **A** should show a reading of _____ millibars.

   (e) The line labelled **B** is an *isobar / contour* and it shows *air pressure / air density*.
       (Circle the correct option in each case.)

   (f) Name each of the features labelled C and D.

       C _____   D _____

(g) The air mass at **E** is a _____ air mass.

(h) On the grid provided describe the weather conditions likely to be found at Dublin, London, Copenhagen and Rome. Refer to atmospheric (air) pressure, wind (direction and strength), cloud and precipitation.

	Air pressure	Wind	Cloud	Precipitation
Dublin				
London				
Copenhagen				
Rome				

1 Explain the **water cycle**, with reference to each of the stages labelled **A, B, C** and **D** in Figure 1.

_____

_____

_____

_____

_____

_____

_____

_____

2 In the boxes provided match each of the terms in Column X with its matching description in Column Y. One pair has been completed for you.

COLUMN X		COLUMN Y	
A	Precipitation	1	Results in the formation of cloud
B	Condensation	2	Returns water to the sea
C	Soakage and run-off	3	Water changes into a gas
D	Evaporation	4	Includes rain, hail, sleet and snow

A	
B	
C	
D	3

3 Name the type of rainfall illustrated by each of the diagrams in Figures 2, 3 and 4.

- Figure 2 _____
- Figure 3 _____
- Figure 4 _____

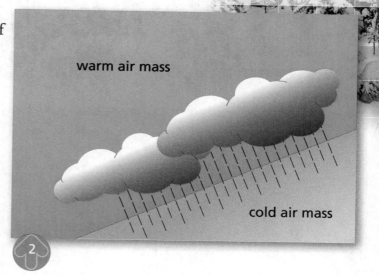

4 Examine Figure 3.

(a) What name is given to the place labelled **Y**? _____

(b) Explain why precipitation would be higher at **X** than at **Y**.

_____

_____

_____

_____

_____

_____

_____

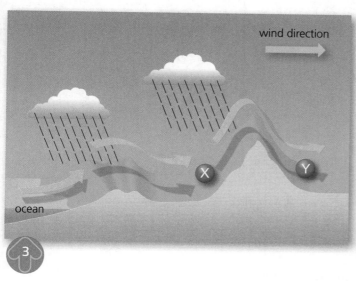

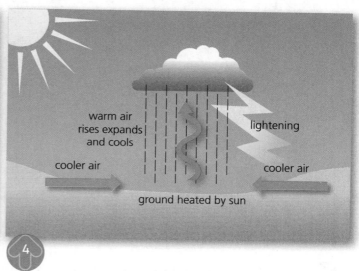

1 Examine Figure 1. In the table below identify the following:
  (a) the name of each of the objects or instruments labelled A–G;
  (b) what each of the instruments B–G is used to measure;
  (c) the unit of measurement related to each of the instruments labelled B–G.

	Object or instrument	What it measures	Unit of measurement
A		————————	————————
B			
C	Thermometer		
D			————————
E			Hours per day
F		Precipitation	
G			

2 A temperature and precipitation table

Examine the table of figures in Figure 2, which shows temperature and precipitation at Caherciveen, Co. Kerry. Temperatures are given in degrees Celsius (°C) and precipitation in millimetres (mm).

Caherciveen, Co. Kerry												
Month	Jan	Feb	Mar	Apr	May	Jun	Jul	Aug	Sep	Oct	Nov	Dec
Temperature (°C)	5	7	9	11	12	14	15	16	14	11	9	6
Precipitation (mm)	92	117	56	19	45	35	23	20	40	75	98	102

2 Temperature and precipitation at Cahirciveen

(a) What is the coldest month? _____

(b) State the temperature of the warmest month. _____

(c) The mean temperature for the months of September, October and November together is *12.6°C / 11.3°C* (circle the correct alternative).

(d) Calculate the mean monthly temperature for the months of December, January and February together. _____

(e) Calculate the mean annual temperature. _____

(f) Calculate the annual temperature range. _____

(g) Explain why temperatures are higher in the summer months. _____

_____

_____

(h) Name the wettest month. _____

(i) Name the month with the least precipitation. _____

(j) State the precipitation for the wettest month. _____

(k) Calculate the total annual precipitation (add up the precipitation for each month of the year).

_____

3 Climate graph

Examine the annual temperature and precipitation graphs in Figure 3.

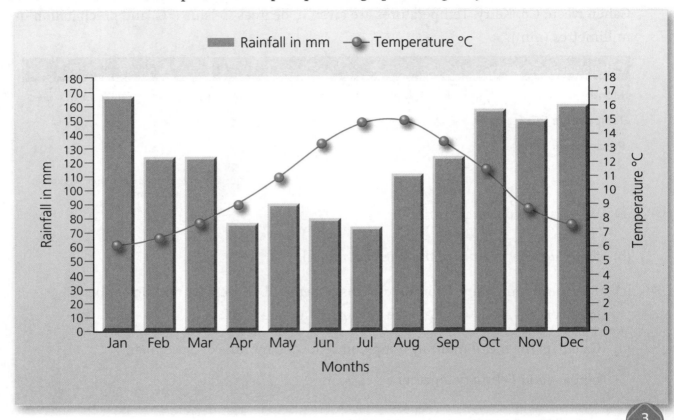

(a) According to the weather chart, which month is the coldest?

(b) Which is the warmest month and what is its mean temperature?

(c) Calculate the annual temperature range.

(d) Calculate the mean temperature for March, April and May together.

(e) Which month gets most precipitation?

(f) Which month is the driest?

(g) State the precipitation in millimetres for the month of November.

4 Climate table and climate graph.

- Figure 4 (on the next page) shows **temperature and precipitation readings** taken at an Irish school over the course of a school week.
- Figure 5 shows a partially completed **climate graph** to illustrate the readings shown in Figure 4.

(a) Use the information in Figure 4 to complete the temperature (line) graph and precipitation (bar) graphs in Figure 5.

5

Temperature (°C)	6	5	11	8	7
Precipitation (mm)	11	3	18	5	0
	Monday	Tuesday	Wednesday	Thursday	Friday

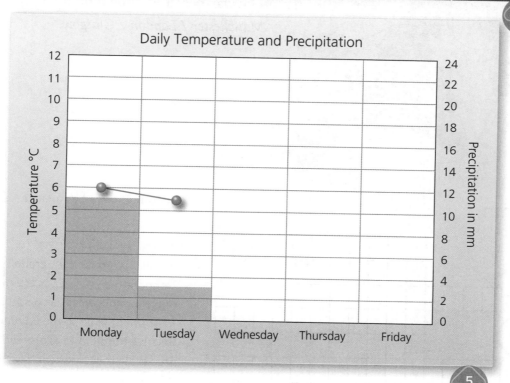

(b) Which day had the highest temperature?

(c) What was the temperature range for the (five-day) week?

(d) What was the mean temperature for the five days?

(e) What was the total precipitation for the five days?

6 The **weather map** in Figure 6 on the next page shows summer temperatures for Ireland and for the United Kingdom.

Circle the correct answer in each of the following sentences:

(a) The lines on the map are *isobars / isotherms / isohels*.

(b) The temperature at **X** is *greater than 16°C / lower than 15°C*.

(c) In most cases, temperatures along the coast are *higher / lower* than inland.

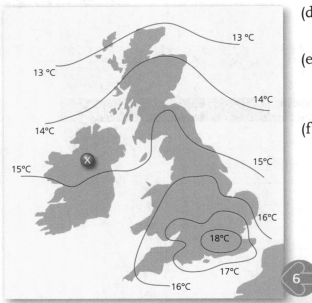

(d) In general, temperatures *increase / decrease* as one goes north.

(e) The range in temperatures between north-west Ireland and south-east England is *less than / more than* 5°C

(f) The warmest area shown on the map is close to *Manchester / London / Glasgow*.

6

7 Funtime

Test your knowledge of Chapter 13 with this bumper word puzzle.

Clue Down

1. Instrument used to measure sunshine.

Clues Across

2. Another word for centigrade.
3. Temperature _ _ _ _ _ is the difference between highest and lowest temperatures.
4. Instrument used to measure temperature.
5. Relative humidity is expressed in these.
6. This scale measures wind in 'forces'.
7. White wooden box with louvred sides.
8. Barometric pressure is measured in these.
9. A hygrometer is used to calculate _ _ _ _ _ _ _ _ humidity.
10. Lines on maps joining places of equal wind speeds.
11. Lines on maps joining places of equal temperatures.
12. Another word for a weather chart.
13. Strong winds may affect the landing or_ _ _ _-off of aircraft.
14. Instrument used to measure wind speed.
15. This is measured in millibars.
16. Used to measure rainfall.
17. Lines on maps joining places of equal sunshine.
18. A depression or 'low'.
19. Opposite of 18 above.
20. Isohyets show places of equal _ _ _ _ _ _ _ _.
21. Instrument used to show wind direction.
22. Precipitation is measured in _ _ _ _ _ _ _ _ _ _ _.
23. Lines on maps joining places of equal barometric pressure.

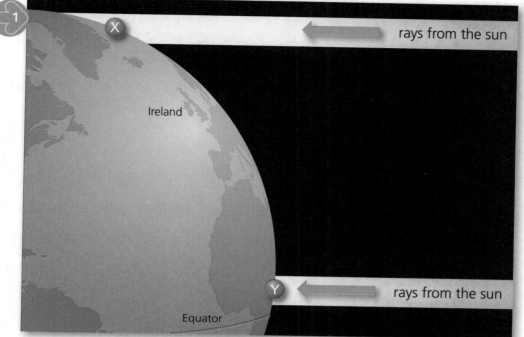

1 Study the diagram in Figure 1.

(a) Is heat from the sun greater at the place labelled **X** or at the place labelled **Y**?

_____

(b) Explain your answer to question (a) above.

_____

_____

_____

_____

2 **Weather Patterns**

Indicate which **three** statements below are correct by ticking (✓) the correct box.

1. The prevailing winds in Ireland are south-westerly.

2. The average annual temperature in Ireland is 20°C.

3. Anticyclones are associated with good weather conditions.

4. The Atlantic Ocean has no influence on weather conditions in Ireland.

5. Relief rainfall is common on the west coast of Ireland.

1, 2, 3 ☐   2, 3, 4 ☐   1, 3, 5 ☐   2, 4, 5 ☐

3 **Some factors affecting climate include:**
- Latitude
- Prevailing winds
- Altitude
- Relief/aspect

Suggested marking scheme

Three factors at *4 marks* each.

Allocate each *4 marks* as follows:
- Clear statment = *2m*
- Development = *1m*
- A further development or example = *1m*

Select **any three** of these factors and explain how each one affects climate. *(12 marks)*

Examine the corrected sample answer on one factor.

- **Latitude**

    The further a place is from the Equator the cooler it is likely to be. **2✓** *Near the Equator, the sun shines almost directly on the land. This means that sunrays are concentrated on quite small areas and give great heat,* **+1✓** *for example in Nigeria in Africa.* **+1✓** *Places far from the equator get oblique sunrays that give little heat because they are spread out over large areas, for example in Antarctica.*

Chapter 12

4 The winter scene in the photograph shows a place in Central Russia that is at approximately the same latitude as Dublin. Explain why winter temperatures here are so different from those in Dublin.

5 Indicate which three of the statements given below are true. *Tick (✓) the correct box.*

1. Ireland's prevailing winds blow towards the north-east.

2. Southerly winds always bring warm, dry conditions to Ireland.

3. The latitude of a place is its angular distance north or south of the equator.

4. Easterly winds bring cold winter conditions to Ireland.

5. The term 'lapse rate' refers to the effect that high winds have on temperatures in mountainous areas.

1, 2, 3 ☐   1, 2, 5 ☐   1, 3, 4 ☐   2, 3, 4 ☐

6 Funtime!

Begin this wheel puzzle on the outside by finding the word referred to in clue 1. Then follow the clues to work inwards to the end. The last letter of each hidden word is also the first letter of the next word. Each of these last/first letters is included to help you. The first and second words are also completed to start you off.

Clues

1. Southerly winds over Ireland are _____ because they come from lower latitudes.

2. This Eastern European capital city has very cold winters.

3. Climate is average _____ over a long period.

4. South-westerly winds might bring this to Ireland.

5. A factor affecting climate.

6. This line of latitude is at the lowest latitude.

7. A factor that affects local climates.

8. This northern EU country has a generally cold climate.

9. A low pressure belt at the Equator.

10. Winds from this direction are usually warm and may bring rain to Ireland.

11. Ireland's summers are not as _____ as those in Mediterranean countries.

12. Ireland's climate is _____ It does not have extremes of temperature.

13. A North African country with a hot desert climate.

14. An instrument used to measure temperatures.

15. This type of rainfall may be common on the seaward slopes of mountains.

1 In the spaces provided, name each of the hot climate types illustrated by the three photographs.

_____   _____   _____

2 Study the map in Figure 1 and write in the correct answers in each case.

(a) The climate type found at A is hot _desert / tundra_.

The climate type found at B is _equatorial / temperate_.

The climate type found at C is _boreal / savannah_.

The climate type found at D is _equatorial / savannah_.

(b) In the spaces provided, name the hot deserts labelled E, F, G and H on the map.

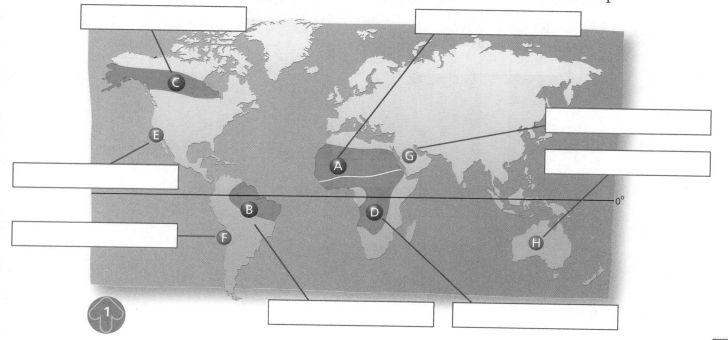

3 (a) Name one type of climate that you have studied. _____

(b) Describe briefly the climate and the vegetation found there. _____

_____

_____

_____

_____

_____

(c) Describe one way in which climate affects people living there. _____

_____

4 Word Puzzle

The map in Figure 2 shows countries of the Sahara desert. Use an atlas or online map to find the names of these countries and use them to solve the word puzzle. The country labelled '1a' on the map is the '1 across' clue on the puzzle. The country labelled '2d' is the '2 down' clue and so on.

1 Select the statements given in the selection box to **complete the diagram** in Figure 1.

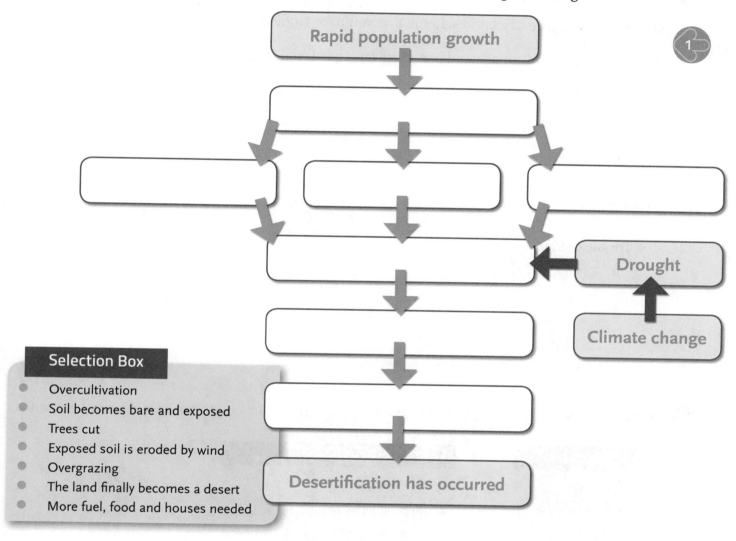

Rapid population growth

Drought

Climate change

Desertification has occurred

Selection Box
- Overcultivation
- Soil becomes bare and exposed
- Trees cut
- Exposed soil is eroded by wind
- Overgrazing
- The land finally becomes a desert
- More fuel, food and houses needed

2 In the boxes provided, match each letter in Column X with the number of its pair in Column Y. One pair has been completed.

COLUMN X	
A	Moving water
B	Severe drought occurred here
C	Low atmospheric pressure
D	High pressure system
E	Sulphur dioxide

COLUMN Y	
1	Acid rain
2	Ascending air
3	Ocean current
4	Dry weather conditions
5	The Sahel

A	
B	5
C	
D	
E	

1 *Some countries use large irrigation schemes to help overcome problems associated with water shortages.*

(a) Name one large irrigation scheme that you have studied. _____

(b) Describe one advantage and one disadvantage of that irrigation scheme.

Advantage: _____

_____

_____

_____

_____

Disadvantage: _____

_____

_____

_____

_____

2 Match each of the items 1–5 in Column X with its pair A–E in Column Y. Use the boxes provided.

	COLUMN X			COLUMN Y			
A	Nasser		1	Artifical watering of land		A	
B	Irrigation		2	River in Egypt		B	
C	Cairo		3	Dam in Egypt		C	
D	Nile		4	Artifical lake in Egypt		D	
E	Aswan		5	City in Egypt		E	

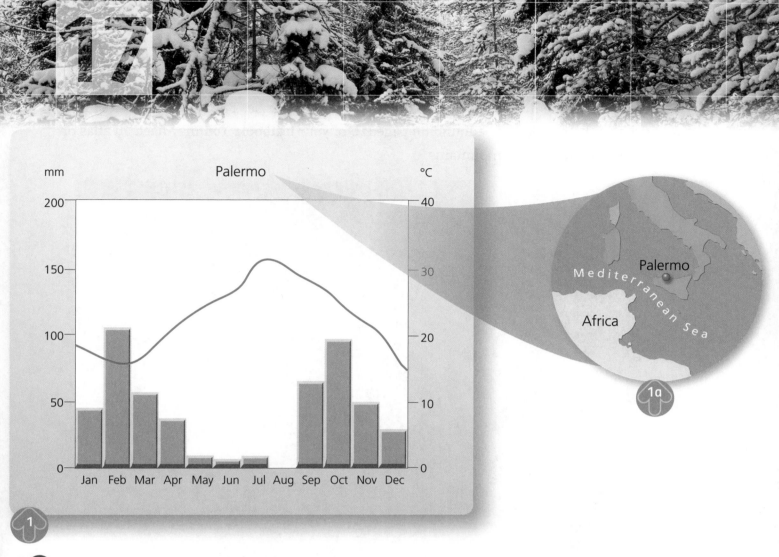

mm   Palermo   °C

1   Figure 1 shows precipitation bars and a temperature graph for Palermo.

(a)   In which *island* and *country* is Palermo? _____

(b)   Name the type of climate at Palermo. _____

(c)   Identify each of the following from Figure 1:

   ●   The hottest month and its temperature _____ _____

   ●   The approximate annual temperature range _____ _____

   ●   The wettest month and its precipitation _____

   ●   The driest month and its precipitation _____

(d)   **Circle the correct options in the statements below:**

In summer, Palermo's climate is *hot / warm* because the city is located at quite *high / low* latitudes and the sun therefore shines from *low / high* in the sky. It is also *damp / dry* because of the presence of *high / low* pressure.

In winter, the city tends to be *cold / mild* and *very wet / moist*. Winds from the *east / west* then sometimes bring *cyclones / anticyclones*, which cause outbreaks of *convectional / frontal* rain.

② Word Puzzle

Mediterranean and mountain tourism

Use the clues on the map (Figure 3) to complete the word puzzle. The countries, tourist regions and cities in the puzzle can be found on page 120 of your **textbook**. You may need an **atlas** or online map to identify the mountains.

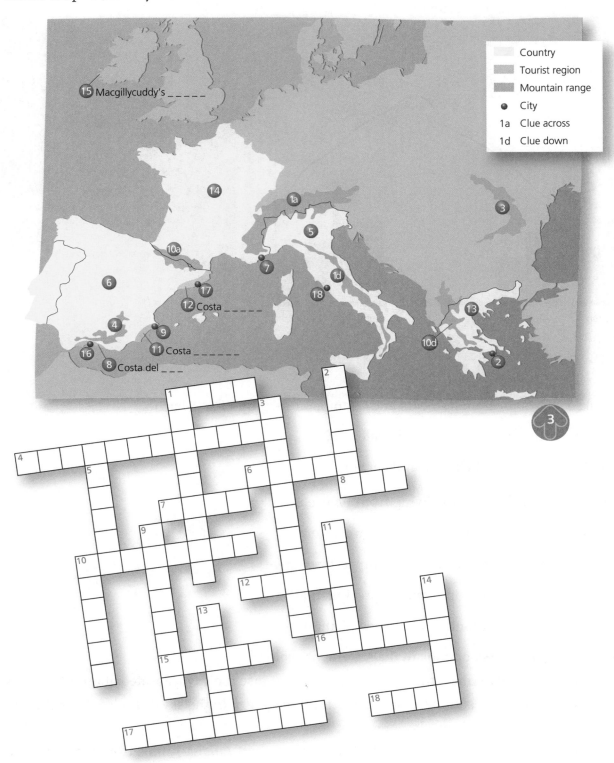

Important!
Junior Certificate Marking Schemes and Model Answers

A   Hints on answering Junior Certificate questions

1   **Read each question very carefully** so that you understand exactly what the question is asking. Take care that your answer remains on the point of the question. Remember that **no** marks will be awarded for off-the-point information.

2   If a question asks you to **name** or to **identify** something, name or identify the object as precisely as possible. Merely name the object. There are **no** extra marks for describing it.

   - **Sample question**: *Name one Mediterranean region in the Southern Hemisphere.*
   - **Full-mark answer**: Central Chile. ✓

3   If you are asked to **describe**, **explain** or otherwise **expand** on something, you must **develop your answer**. A developed answer should include *a statement and up to three development points* of information at Higher Level. A statement and one or two development points will suffice at Ordinary Level. Each point of information can be short and simple, provided it is relevant. Points may include **examples** or refer to reasons for something.

   - **Sample question**: *Explain how the natural vegetation of Mediterranean lands is suited to the Mediterranean climate.*
   - **Full-mark answer**: *Some trees have small waxy leaves. ✓ The olive tree is an example. ✓ Such trees do not lose moisture through transpiration. ✓ Transpiration is the loss of moisture through the bark. ✓*

4   In all examinations, **manage your time carefully** so that you answer all the questions required of you as perfectly as you can.

5   **Have confidence**. Most Junior Certificate questions are straightforward, so do not look for 'hidden tricks' in them. If you study your textbook well, you will cover the entire Junior Certificate course and are likely to find almost all questions quite easy.

> *It is important to understand how Junior Certificate examination questions are marked and to be aware of what must be written in order to obtain full marks for an answer. Given here are:*
> *(a) some general hints on how to answer questions well;*
> *(b) a sample Junior Certificate question with marking scheme;*
> *(c) a sample 'full-mark' answer to a Junior Certificate question.*

B   Sample Junior Certificate examination question

The Mediterranean area has hot, dry summers and mild, moist winters.

Q   Explain why weather conditions are so different in
summer and in winter in Mediterranean areas.

(10 marks) (J.C. Higher Level)

> To ensure full
> marks always try
> to write one extra
> development.

Marking scheme

This question asks for reasons for the main
features of Mediterranean climate in summer
and in winter.

The *10 marks* set aside for the question
include *5 marks* for development explanation(s)
of summer conditions and *5 marks* for
development explanation(s) of winter
conditions.

Each *5 marks* is awarded as follows:
- Statement = *2 marks*
- First development = *1 mark*
- Second development = *1 mark*
- Third development = *1 mark*

C   Full-Mark Answer

Summers are hot and dry because:

- The area is less than 40 degrees from the Equator. (2 marks)
- Therefore the sun is high in the sky and gives great heat. (1 mark)
- High pressure dominates the area in summer. (1 mark)
- This brings dry, settled weather. (1 mark)

Winters are mild and moist because:

- Even in winter, the sun is high enough in the sky to give quite warm conditions. (2 marks)
- Prevailing winds blow in from the Atlantic. (1 mark)
- These winds carry depressions. (1 mark)
- Depressions bring wet, unsettled conditions. (1 mark)

> Now answer the
> two Junior Certificate
> questions on the opposite
> page and correct them using
> the marking schemes
> indicated.

3 Study the diagram below.

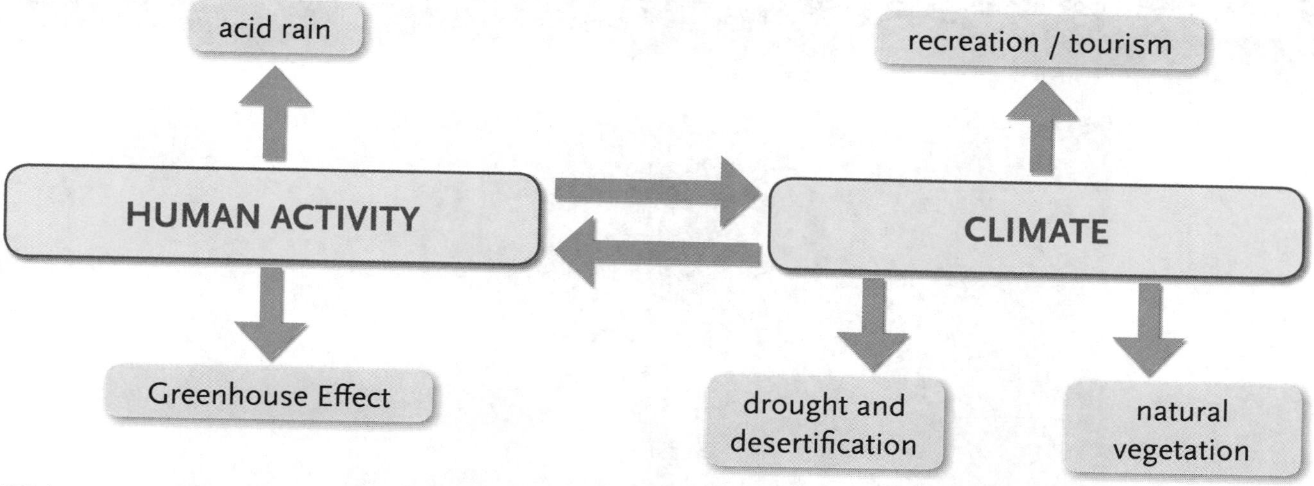

acid rain

recreation / tourism

HUMAN ACTIVITY

CLIMATE

Greenhouse Effect

drought and desertification

natural vegetation

Write two sentences to describe what the diagram shows. *(6 marks)*

(a) _____

_____

_____

(b) _____

_____

_____

Marking scheme

Two sentences at *3 marks* each. Each sentence should refer to at least two linkages (connections) given in the diagram.

Marking scheme

How a warm climate attracts tourists = *6 marks*

How a cold climate attracts tourists = *6 marks*

Each 6 marks is *awarded as follows:*

Statement = *2 marks*

First development = *1 mark*

Second development = *1 mark*

A country named = *2 marks*

4 *The tourist industry of many countries depends on climate.*

Explain how (a) a warm climate and (b) a cold climate can help to attract tourists to a country. Name a country in each case. *(12 marks)*

Reminder:
Try to include one ***extra development*** *in each explanation.*

(a) _____

_____

_____

_____

(b) _____

_____

_____

_____

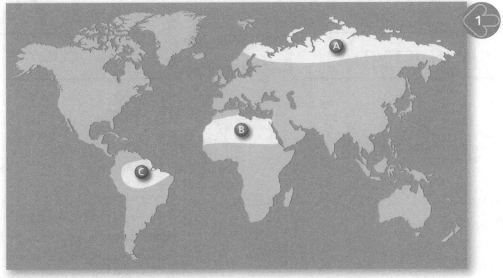

1. (a) Name each of the climate types **A**, **B** and **C** shown on Figure 1.

A _____

B _____

C _____

(b) Explain the climatic characteristics of **any one** climate type that you have studied.

_____

_____

_____

_____

_____

_____

_____

2. Circle the correct answer in **each** of the following statements:

(a) Coniferous trees have adapted to climate by *keeping / losing* their needles in winter.

(b) Coniferous trees have adapted to where they grow by having *long / short* roots.

(c) Coniferous trees are better suited to *upland / lowland* regions in Ireland.

Chapter 18

3 Look at the climate figures in Figure 2.

(a) Which of the following climate types is most likely to be shown by the figures?

Savannah type ☐
Tundra type ☐
Warm temperate oceanic type ☐
Cool temperate oceanic type ☐

(b) The *maximum monthly temperature* is

_____.

(c) The *coldest* month is _____.

(d) Which of the following is the correct *annual temperature range* for this weather station?

32°C ☐   12°C ☐   −24°C ☐   −12°C ☐

(e) The *minimum monthly temperature* is _____.

(f) The *wettest month* is _____.

(g) Which of the following is the correct total annual precipitation figure for this weather station?

23mm ☐   94mm ☐   104mm ☐   20.5mm ☐

Month	Mean temp (°C)	Mean precip. (mm)
January	−26	5.0
February	−28	2.5
March	−26	2.5
April	−18	2.5
May	−8	2.5
June	1	7.5
July	4	23.0
August	4	20.0
September	−1	13.0
October	−8	13.0
November	−17	7.5
December	−24	5.0

4 Use the information in Figure 2 to complete the precipitation graph in Figure 3.

1 Indicate whether each of the following statements is true or false (circle the *True* or *False* alternative in each case).

(a) Relatively little natural vegetation exists in Western Europe.   *True / False*

(b) Hot, wet regions of the world tend to have thick forests.   *True / False*

(c) As temperatures increase, vegetation usually becomes more scarce.   *True / False*

(d) Most types of vegetation will not grow below 4°C.   *True / False*

In the boxes provided in Figure 1, explain how climate affects natural vegetation.

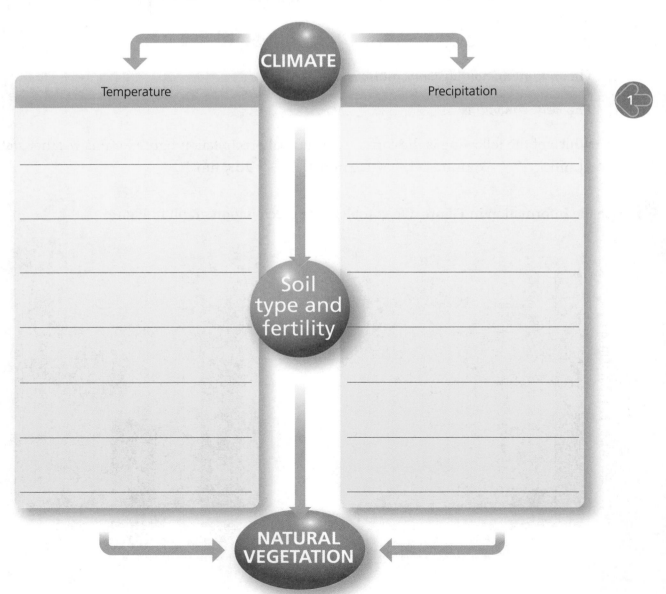

1 The divided bar chart shows the composition of soil.

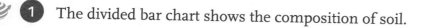

| Mineral particles | air | water | Plant Remains |

0% 5% 10% 15% 20% 25% 30% 35% 40% 45% 50% 55% 60% 65% 70% 75% 80% 85% 90% 95% 100%

1

(a) Label the pie chart in Figure 2, using the information on the divided bar in Figure 1.

(b) What percentage of the bar chart shows:

- mineral particles _____

- air _____

- water _____

- plant remains _____

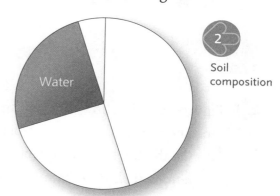

2

Soil composition

Water

2 Choose *three terms* from the selection box to fill the gaps in the extract below.

The breakdown of plant litter into _____ helps to fertilise soil. Processes such as _____ may damage soil fertility by causing nutrients to seep below the reach of plant roots. _____ are a type of soil commonly found in damp highland areas in Ireland.

Selection Box

- leaching
- mineral particles
- micro-organisms
- podzols
- humus
- hard pans

3 **How soil is formed**

Use the words in the selection box to fill in the blank spaces in Figure 3.

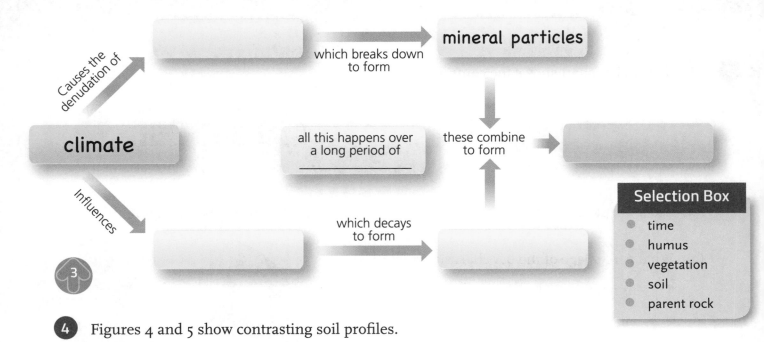

climate

Causes the denudation of

which breaks down to form

mineral particles

all this happens over a long period of _____

these combine to form

Influences

which decays to form

Selection Box

- time
- humus
- vegetation
- soil
- parent rock

4 Figures 4 and 5 show contrasting soil profiles.

One shows the profile of podzols and the other of brown soils.

(a) On the lines provided label the following in their correct places: *B-horizon; brown A-horizon; hardpan; plentiful humus near surface; greyish A-horizon; C-horizon (bedrock); leaching; plant litter*

(b) In the boxes provided, label the *podzol profile* and *brown soils profile*.

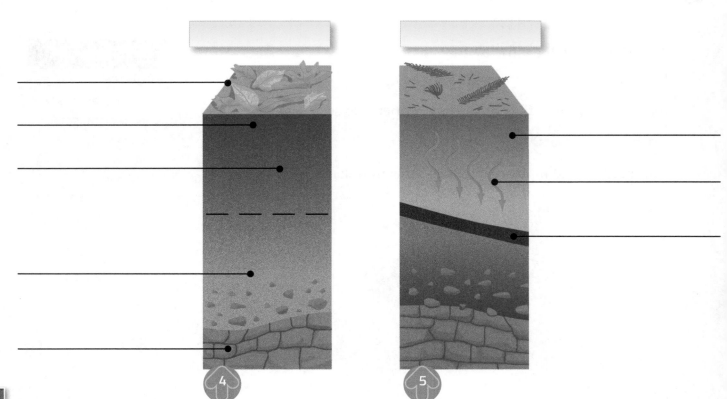

Chapter 20

Test yourself . . . . . . with this Junior Cert Higher Level question. Use the official marking scheme and sample answers to help you.

 5 (a) Explain two ways in which soil is important to humans. *(4 marks)*

Starter sample answer:

Soils are needed to grow farm crops, **1** ✓

which provide us with the food we need. **1** ✓

Official Marking Scheme

(a) Two explanations get 2 marks each. In each explanation give 1 mark for a statement and 1 mark for a development.

Reminder: Try to write one **extra** development in each explanation.

Now explain two other ways:

1 _____

_____

2 _____

_____

(b) With reference to *two* of the following factors, explain their role in soil formation:

- original rock
- climate
- micro-organisms
- vegetation *(6 marks)*

Official Marking Scheme

(b) Two explanations get 3 marks each. In each explanation give 2 marks for a statement and 1 mark for a development.

Starter sample answer:

The original rock is weathered and eroded by frost, water, etc. **2** ✓

It breaks down into small mineral particles, which make up part of the soil. **1** ✓

Now write about two other factors:

1 _____

_____

2 _____

_____

6 Wordgame

Clues Across

2. Process involving the breakdown of plant litter into humus
4. Colour of Ireland's most common soil type
6. Air in soil includes this life-giving gas
7. Iron oxide
9. Tropical __ __ __ soil is found in the tropics
10. Vertical section of soil from the surface downwards
11. This continent contains lots of the soil type in clue 9
12. Impermeable layer caused by leaching
17. Soil type in clue 9 can be found in this type of climate
19. Factor in the formation of soil
23. Fertile soil in A horizons of soil profiles
25. Makes up about five per cent of soil

Clues Down

1. Principal ingredients of soils
3. Soils found in any Irish highland areas
5. Soil nutrient
8. Twigs, leaves, etc. on the surface of soil
13. Important soil-living animals
14. Major factor in the formation of soil
15. Dominates C horizons of soil profiles
16. Type of forest in which brown soil was originally formed
18. Process in which nutrients are washed down through soil
20. Soil type common near Ireland's west coast
21. Ingredient that makes up about a quarter of soil
22. Soil type found in counties such as Clare and Antrim
24. Another major ingredient of soil

Examine the Ordnance Survey map of the Killarney area on page 156 of your textbook. Questions 1 to 8 below relate to this map.

Tick (✓) the correct box for each of questions 1 to 7.

1 The shortest distance between Heron Island (V 93 89) and Ash Island (V 96 87) is:

2.90 km ☐   3.30 km ☐   3.53 km ☐   6.22 km ☐

2 The length of the N71 road from where it enters the south of the map at V 914 810 to where it crosses the River Flesk at V 967 894 is approximately:

11.25 km ☐   12.25 km ☐   13.25 km ☐   14.25 km ☐

3 The area represented by the map is:

81 km² ☐   99 km² ☐   121 km² ☐   125 km² ☐

4 The area represented by that part of the map which is west of Easting 95 and north of Northing 88 is:

16 km² ☐   20 km² ☐   36 km² ☐   44 km² ☐

5 The approximate area of Lough Leane and Muckross Lake together is:

5 km² ☐   13 km² ☐   19 km² ☐   25 km² ☐

6 The direction from Brown Island (V 923 897) to Cow Island (V 955 874) is:

South-east ☐   North-west ☐

South-west ☐   South-south-west ☐

7 That part of the River Flesk which flows at grid square V 96 88 flows in a:

northerly direction ☐   southerly direction ☐

north-north-easterly direction ☐   south-westerly direction ☐

8 Full Junior Certificate-style Question, Marking Scheme and Model Answer

On page 70 you will find the *OS map* of the *Ardee area* which appeared in a Junior Certificate examination. Below is a full set of questions, marking schemes and sample 'full-mark' answers relating to that map. Examine the map and the information given below. This will help you to understand what you have to do to obtain full marks in your examination answers.

The Questions

1. Study the Ordnance Survey map of the Ardee area.
   (a) What is the distance in kilometres along the N2 roadway from the junction with the third class road (N 994 848) to the junction with the R170 road (N 963 903)? *(4 marks)*

   (b) If you were travelling in a straight line to Ardee from the following places, in which direction would you be travelling in each case?
   (i) Philibenstown (O 0094)
   (ii) Blakestown Cross Roads (N 965 878)
   (iii) Knocklore (N 931 953) *(6 marks)*

2. Using evidence from the map only, give three reasons why Ardee developed at this location. In your answer refer to both the past and the present. *(12 marks)*

3. (a) Name the rural settlement pattern that exists at N98 85 on the map. *(2 marks)*
   (b) Why is there no settlement at N 97 91 on the map? *(2 marks)*
   (c) Give the height in metres of the highest pont on the map. Give a six-figure location for this point. *(4 marks)*

> Remember that the answers given to questions 2 below are only samples of information that could be used to obtain full marks. In these cases, other relevant points of information could also be used.

The Marking Scheme

1 (a) Award 4 marks for any answer within a range of 7.0 km to 7.5 km only.

(b) Award 2 marks each for these three directions only:
   (i) South-west
   (ii) North
   (iii) South-east

2 Award 4 marks for each of three reasons. At least one reason must refer to the **present** and at least one reason must refer to the **past**.
Allocate each 4 marks as follows:
Statement = 2 marks
Development = 1 mark
Map evidence = 1 mark

> Try to write one extra development for 'mark security'.

3 (a) Award 2 marks for stating that the settlement pattern is linear.

(b) Award 2 marks for an answer that says or suggests that the area is poorly drained or is liable to flood or might be flooded by the river or rivers.

(c) • Award 2 marks for correct height (225 metres).
   • Award 2 marks for grid reference N 977 848 or N 977 849
   • Award 1 mark if the grid letter and either the full Easting or the full Northing numbers are given correctly.
   • Award 1 mark if N 97 84 is given correctly.

Full-Mark Answers

1 (a) 7.3 km **4** ✓

(b) (i) South-west **2** ✓
   (ii) North **2** ✓
   (iii) South-east **2** ✓

 10/10

2 (a) Ardee was once a defence point. **2** ✓ There are castles to be found, **1** ✓ for example at N 962 905. **1** ✓ **2** ✓

(b) It is a meeting point of roads, for example the N2 and N52. Where **1** ✓ roads meet trade develops and settlements grow. **1** ✓

(c) It is a bridging point on the River Dee at N 963 904. Roads meet to **2** ✓ **1** ✓ cross the bridge. **1** ✓

12/10

3 (a) It is a linear pattern. **2** ✓

(b) There are rivers there and they might flood the area so that **2** ✓ people could not live there.

(c) The highest point is 225 metres. **2** ✓ It is at N 977 848. **2** ✓

 8/8

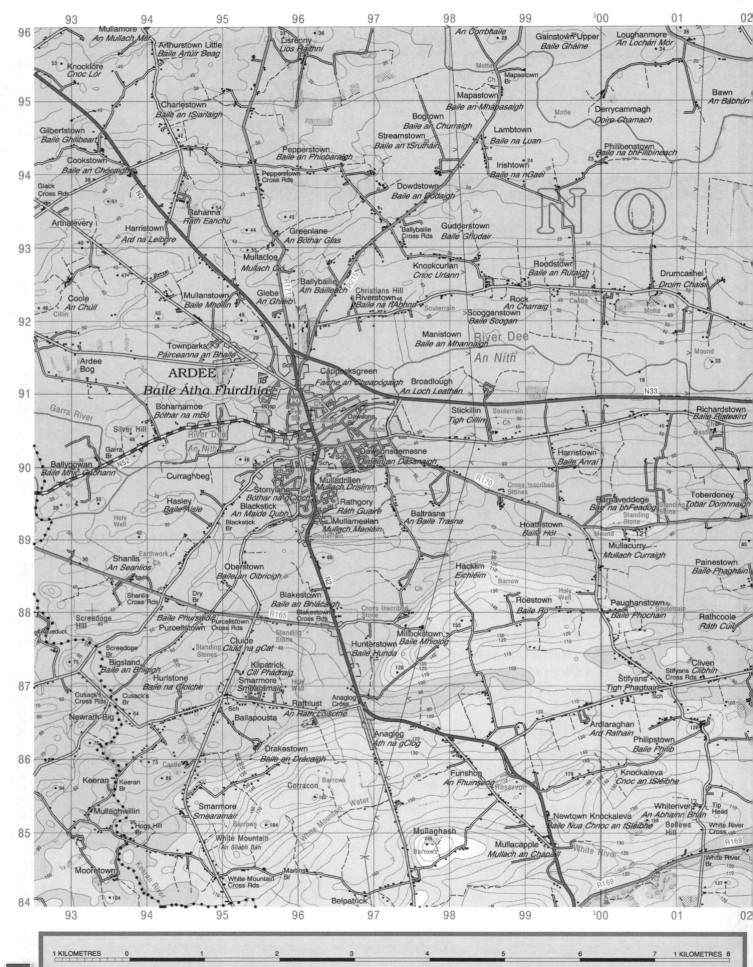

Ardee, Co. Louth

9 **For You to Do – a Full Junior Certificate Ordnance Survey Map Question (with Marking Scheme)**

On pages 68 and 69 you examined Junior Certificate marking schemes and full-mark answers.

On page 157 of your **textbook** you will find the *OS map* of the *Sligo/Rosses Point* area used in a Junior Certificate examination. Use this map to answer the Junior Certificate Higher Level questions given below. Try to achieve full-mark answers with the help of the marking schemes provided.

> **Marking scheme**
>
> **A** Two different kinds of tourist attraction, one in Drumcliff and one in Rosses Point, will get *4 marks* each. (Note that each tourist attraction must be apparent on the map.) *Allocate each 4 marks as follows:*
> - Tourist attraction named = *2 marks*
> - Development/description = *1 mark*
> - Grid reference location on map = *1 mark*

> Reminder: Try to write one extra development in each explanation or description.

A. The areas around Drumcliff (G 67 42) and Rosses Point (G 63 40) attract tourists for different reasons. Using Ordnance Survey map evidence **only**, describe one type of attraction provided by Rosses Point and a different type of tourist attraction in Drumcliff. (*8 marks*)

Answer: _____

_____

_____

_____

B. (i) What is the distance, in kilometres, along the N15 road from its junction with the R291 (G 69 36) to Drumcliff Bridge (G 67 42)? (*4 marks*)

   (ii) Would a climb of *Kings Mountain* (G 703 442) *from the south-east* be steeper than a climb of *Knocknarea* (G 626 346) *from the east*? Explain briefly how you know. (*6 marks*)

Answer (i): _____

_____

Answer (ii): _____

> **Marking scheme**
>
> **B** (i) *Four marks* for correct or near correct answer.
>
>   (ii) Allow *2 marks* for identifying the less steep slope.
>   Allow *4 marks* for 'how you know'.
>   Allocate these marks as follows:
>   - Statement = *2 marks*
>   - Development or map (grid) reference = *2 marks*

C. The processes of **erosion** and **deposition** have influenced the area shown on the map. With reference to **two** specific features explain this statement. Use map evidence to support your answer. (*12 marks*)

Answer: _____

_____

_____

_____

_____

_____

_____

_____

_____

> **Marking scheme**
>
> **C** *Six marks* each should be allocated for a specific feature of erosion and a specific feature of deposition.
> *Allocate each 6 marks as follows:*
> - Feature identified = *2 marks*
> - Grid reference location of feature = *2 marks*
> - Development/description = *2 marks*

10 **Another question relating to the Sligo/Rosses Point map**

(See page 157 of your textbook.)

Imagine that plans have been made to construct a large hotel and leisure centre at the place located at G 684 380 on the Sligo area map:

(a) Describe two advantages that this site might have for such a development.

- _____

  _____

- _____

  _____

(b) Describe two objections that local people might have to this development.

- _____

  _____

- _____

  _____

11 Draw a sketch map

On this page draw a sketch map of the **Sligo area map** that appears on **page 157 of your textbook**. Draw your sketch to half the scale (half the length and half the width) of the original map. On your sketch map show and label each of the following:

- The built-up area of Rosses Point;
- The N15 national primary road;
- The Drumcliff River;
- A golf course near Rosses Point;
- A coniferous plantation on the north-west of the map;
- Shade in all land over 200 metres in altitude on the northeast of the map.

Hints

- Give your map a title.
- Indicate north with an arrow.
- Draw in the coast before showing any required feature.
- Centre your map on the page, so that you can write your labels outside the map, with arrows pointing in to the required features shown on the map.

12 Aerial photographs, maps and change over time

Photographs and maps can demonstrate how landscape changes over time.

Figure 1 shows the area around Ballycotton, Co. Cork. It consists partly of a modern aerial photograph and partly of a map made in 1841. The coastline in 1841 is shown as a red line. Today's coastline is shown as a green line. Use the information in Figure 1 to circle the **correct alternatives** in the description below.

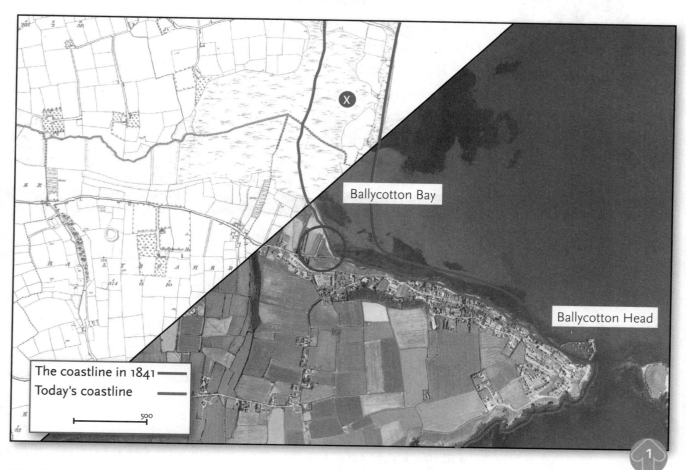

Ballycotton Bay

Ballycotton Head

The coastline in 1841 ——
Today's coastline ——

500

1

The physical landscape of the Ballycotton area has changed greatly since 1841. The **sea / a great river** *is mainly responsible for the change. Much land has been* **gained / lost** *along the coast because of* **sea erosion / deposition**. *The greatest change is the* **Ballycotton Head / Ballycotton Bay** *area. In the place labelled 'X', the distance between the old and present-day coastline is approximately* **50 / 500** *metres. which is* **half / a quarter** *of a kilometre. The Ballycotton Head area suffered* **much less / no** *erosion because it consists mainly of sandstone cliffs. These are* **more / less resistant** *to erosion than the clays that make up much of the bay area.*

The retreating coastline has disrupted the course of ancient roads. The circled area on the photograph shows **three / two** *roads ending abruptly on the coastline. One was the old road to Ballycotton village. The other travelled* **northwest / north** *across what is now Ballycotton Bay. The land these roads travelled through has long since been devoured by the sea.*

23-24

① Full Junior Certificate Aerial Photograph Question, Marking Scheme and Model Answer

On pages 70 and 71 you will find the OS map and the aerial photograph of the *Ardee area* that appeared in a Junior Certificate examination. Below is the Higher Level Junior Certificate aerial photograph question from that examination, together with its marking scheme and sample 'full-mark' answers. Examine these. They will help you to understand what you have to do to obtain full marks in your examination answers.

The Questions	The Marking Scheme
① Using the photograph only, draw a sketch map of the part of Ardee town shown. On the map mark and identify the following places: (a) two connecting roads; (b) a church and graveyard; (c) a historic building; (d) grain silos; (e) a timber storage area. *(10 marks)*	**①** Award 2 marks for *locating and naming* each of the five features demanded. Deduct 1 mark if the sketch map is not correctly framed.
② (a) *The main street in Ardee runs across the photograph from left middleground to right middleground.* With reference to the photograph, give two pieces of evidence to support the statement that this is Ardee's main street. *(4 marks)* (b) Briefly explain one advantage and one disadvantage in living along the main street of a town like Ardee. *(6 marks)*	**②** (a) Award *2 marks each for two pieces of evidence.* (In the case of each 2 marks, allow 1 mark for a statement and one mark for evidence from the photograph.) (b) Award *3 marks for one advantage.* (2 marks for statement and 1 mark for development.) Award *3 marks for one disadvantage.* (2 marks for statement and 1 mark for development.)
③ The local authority for this area is going to build a new shopping centre in the area shown on the photograph. (a) Identify the part of the photograph in which you would locate this shopping centre. *(2 marks)* (b) With reference to both the photograph and the map, give one advantage and one disadvantage of this location. *(8 marks)*	**③** (a) Award *2 marks for identifying a suitable location.* (b) Award *4 marks for one advantage.* (Give 2 marks for a statement, 1 mark for development and 1 mark for map/ photograph evidence.) Award *4 marks for one disadvantage.* (Give 2 marks for a statement, 1 mark for development and 1 mark for map/photographic evidence.)

* Answer (b) must include at least one map reference and one photograph reference.

Sketch map of Ardee

N

grain silos

a historic building

church and graveyard

two connecting roads

a timber storage area

Remember that the answers to the questions given below are only samples of the information that would be used to obtain full marks. Other relevant points of information could also be used.

Correct the answers below using the marking scheme on p. 76.

Full-Mark Answers

① 1

② (a) (i) It is the busiest street in town. This is shown by the heavy vehicle traffic on the street in the centre middleground.

(ii) Buildings are higher here than on other streets. There are three-storey buildings on the street in the left middleground.

(b) (i) One advantage is that people living on the main street would be close to important services, such as shops and the church in the left middleground. They could easily access those services on foot.

(ii) One disadvantage is that people might be disturbed by traffic congestion, noise or air pollution from the heavy traffic, which can be seen on this street. Traffic might be a danger to children living on Main Street.

③ (a) A suitable location would be in the centre background (by the large cereal field at the edge of the town).

(b) (i) One advantage of this location is that it is connected to the town by a road. The map shows that it is also close to the N2 national primary roadway, which would provide easy access.

(ii) One disadvantage of this location is that it would mean the destruction of farmland. The photograph shows that this flat land produces cereal crops, which indicates that the land is fertile.

2 **For You to Do – A Full Junior Certificate Aerial Photograph Question (with Marking Scheme)**

On pages 76 and 77 you examined marking schemes and sample answers for a full Junior Certificate aerial photograph question.

On page 189 of your *textbook* you will find the aerial photograph of the *Ballina* used in a Junior Certificate examination. Use this *photograph* (along with the OS map of the *Ballina area* on page 188 of your textbook) to answer the Junior Certificate Higher Level question given below. Try to achieve full-mark answers with the help of the marking schemes provided.

Marking scheme

A River Moy = *1 mark*
2 bridges = *1 mark + 1 mark*
2 connecting streets = *1 mark + 1 mark*
church with spire = *1 mark*
industrial estate = *1 mark*
terraced housing = *1 mark*
shopping centre = *1 mark*
car park = *1 mark*
shape of sketch = *2 marks*
Total = *12 marks*

 A. Draw a sketch map on this page of the area shown on the **aerial photograph**. Show and name the following: (i) the River Moy and two bridges; (ii) two connecting streets; (iii) a church with a spire; (iv) an industrial estate; (v) an area of terraced housing; (vi) a shopping centre and car park. (*12 marks*)

2 Sketch map of Ballina area

B. **The town of Ballina provides a variety of services.**
With reference to the OS map only, describe three of these services. (*12 marks*)

Answers:

(a) _____

_____

_____

_____

_____

(b) _____

_____

_____

(c) _____

_____

_____

_____

Marking scheme

Ⓑ Three descriptions at *4 marks* each.
Allocate each *four marks* as follows:
- *2 marks* for a statement;
- *1 mark* for a development;
- *1 mark* for reference to the map.

Reminder:
Try to write **one** extra development in each explanation or description.

C. It is proposed to redevelop the area of unused land on the right side of the river, in the right middleground of the photograph.

(a) Suggest a suitable use for this land.

(b) Explain two reasons for your choice.
(*6 marks*)

Marking scheme

Ⓒ (i) Give *2 marks* for a suitable land use stated.
(ii) Give *2 marks* each for two reasons given.

(a) _____

_____

_____

(b) • _____

_____

• _____

_____

  1 Match each of the letters in **Column X** with its matching number in **Column Y**. One match has been made for you.

COLUMN X		COLUMN Y	
A	Natural decrease	1	The average number of people per square kilometre
B	Population density	2	The number of live births per 1,000 population in one year
C	Population explosion	3	When the death rate is larger than the birth rate
D	Birth rate	4	Very rapid population growth

A	3
B	
C	
D	

How to draw a line graph (trend graph)

Study the tips on this page before answering question 2(v) on the next page.

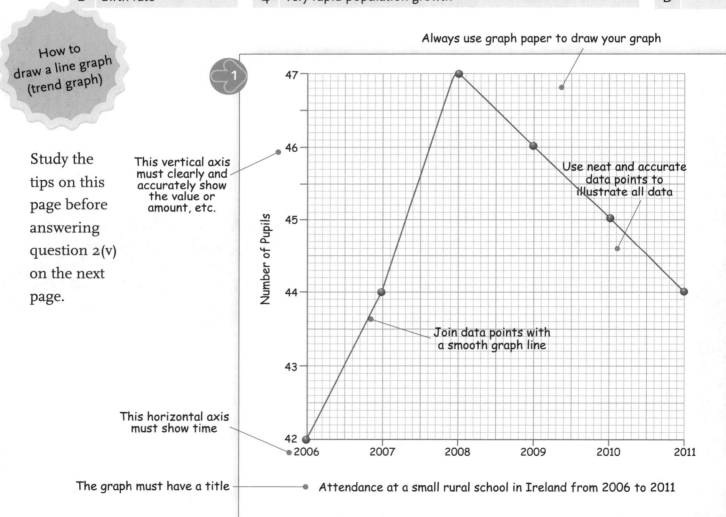

Always use graph paper to draw your graph

This vertical axis must clearly and accurately show the value or amount, etc.

Use neat and accurate data points to illustrate all data

Join data points with a smooth graph line

This horizontal axis must show time

The graph must have a title

Attendance at a small rural school in Ireland from 2006 to 2011

Chapter 25

2 The table shows the populations of four Irish counties at different times.

	1986	1996	2006	2011
Galway	179,223	190,006	232,334	250,334
Mayo	114,985	111,497	124,648	130,638
Sligo	57,556	55,848	61,891	65,393
Leitrim	27,187	25,564	28,841	31,798

(a) Which county had the largest population in 2006? _____

(b) Which county had the smallest population in 1996? _____

(c) Which county had the smallest increase in population between 1986 and 2006?

_____

(d) Name the county with the largest increase in population between 1986 and 2011 and calculate that increase.

County: _____   Increase: _____

(e) On the graph paper below draw a line graph to illustrate population change in Co. Leitrim between 1986 and 2011. Show population to the nearest thousand. Show suitable axes and give your graph a title.

You may need to study the tips in Figure 1 before drawing this line graph

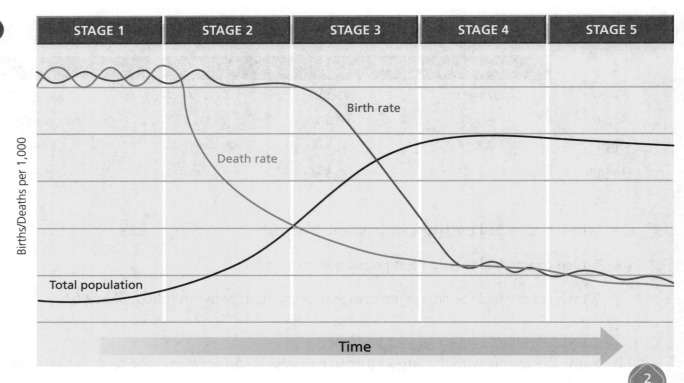

(a) What name is given to this diagram? _____

(b) At which stage of the diagram is the death rate at its highest? _____

(c) At which stage of the diagram is the total population growing most rapidly? _____

(d) At which stage is there a natural decrease in the population? _____

(e) Briefly explain each of the following:

- Why the death rate fluctuates (goes up and down) at Stage 1 _____

  _____

- Why the death rate declines rapidly at Stage 2 _____

  _____

- Why the birth rate declines at Stage 3 _____

  _____

(f) Circle the correct answer in each of the statements below:

- Stage 1 is referred to as the *high fluctuating stage / low fluctuating stage*.

- Many Third World countries are at *Stage 3 / Stage 5* of the population cycle.

- Stage 4 represents the population trends in *developed countries / developing countries*.

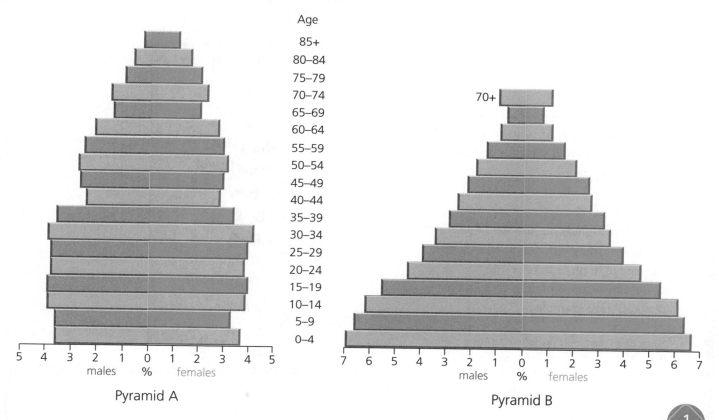

26

1 **Population pyramids of two countries**

Pyramid A

Pyramid B

(a) Which of the two pyramids presents the population of a poor developing country?

_____

(b) Name one country with a population structure similar to Pyramid A.

_____

(c) Explain one reason why Pyramid B has a wider base than Pyramid A.

_____

_____

(d) What percentage of the population shown in Pyramid B is under 5 years old? _____

(e) Describe **two** ways in which governments use population pyramids.

• _____

• _____

2 Class Project on Population Structure

Learning intentions:

- For each student to create a population pyramid that illustrates the population structure of all class members' families.
- For each student to comment on the population structure illustrated.

Steps:

In class:

1. The project is explained to students.
2. Each student draws an 'unticked' copy of a 'population pyramid skeleton' similar to that shown in Figure 3.

At home:

3. Each student finds out the age of each person in his/her family*. The student uses this knowledge to place ticks on the appropriate age-group sections of his/her 'pyramid skeleton' (see example in Figure 3).

*Include in the family the following living people: Parents or guardians, brothers, sisters, step brothers, step sisters, foster brothers, foster sisters, grandparents. Count all the above even if they are not living in the home. Also count any other person who is living permanently in the home.

In class:

4. A large copy of the pyramid skeleton is placed on the whiteboard. Each student enters his/her 'ticks' on this large copy.
5. The total number of ticks for each gender-total in each age-group is then calculated and written on the appropriate age-group area (see example in Figure 4). Each student copies these totals on the appropriate age-group areas of his/her own pyramid skeleton.
6. Each student is given a sheet of graph paper.

Sample of one female student's research on family age structure. These results are 'ticked' on the population pyramid skeleton in Figure 3 below

2

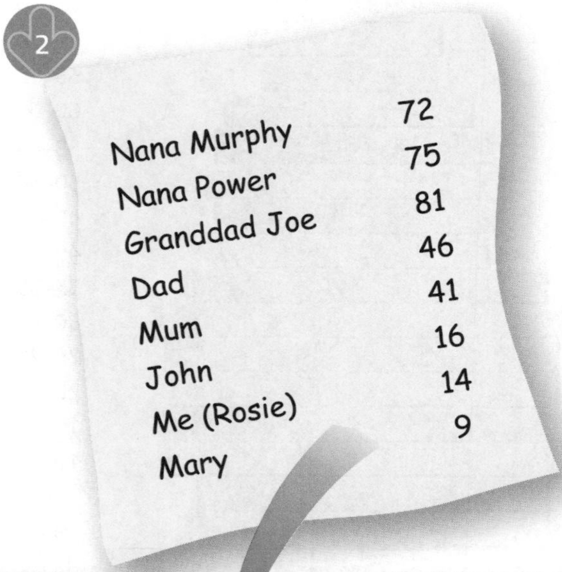
Nana Murphy 72
Nana Power 75
Granddad Joe 81
Dad 46
Mum 41
John 16
Me (Rosie) 14
Mary 9

Males	Age	Females
✓	80+	
	70-79	✓ ✓
	60-69	
	50-59	
✓	40-49	✓
	30-39	
	20-29	
✓	10-19	✓
	0-9	✓

3 Population pyramid 'skeleton' (filled by one student)

Chapter 26

At home:

7. Each student uses the graph paper and a pencil to create a population pyramid based on the age-group totals calculated in class (see example in Figure 5).

Each population pyramid should have:

- A suitable horizontal scale along the base;
- Clearly labelled age-group sectors up the middle;
- Neat and accurate age-bars for both males and females in all age groups;
- A title.

(See Figure 5)

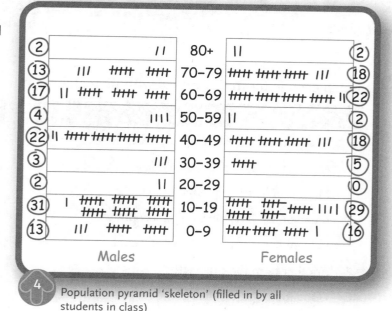

Males	80+	Females
(2) ‖	80+	‖ (2)
(13) ‖‖ ⅲ⅃⅃ ⅲ⅃⅃	70–79	ⅲ⅃⅃ ⅲ⅃⅃ ⅲ⅃⅃ ‖‖ (18)
(17) ‖ ⅲ⅃⅃ ⅲ⅃⅃ ⅲ⅃⅃	60–69	ⅲ⅃⅃ ⅲ⅃⅃ ⅲ⅃⅃ ⅲ⅃⅃ ‖ (22)
(4) ‖‖‖	50–59	‖ (2)
(22) ‖ ⅲ⅃⅃ ⅲ⅃⅃ ⅲ⅃⅃ ⅲ⅃⅃	40–49	ⅲ⅃⅃ ⅲ⅃⅃ ⅲ⅃⅃ ‖‖ (18)
(3) ‖‖	30–39	ⅲ⅃⅃ (5)
(2) ‖	20–29	(0)
(31) ‖ ...	10–19	... (29)
(13) ‖‖ ⅲ⅃⅃ ⅲ⅃⅃	0–9	ⅲ⅃⅃ ⅲ⅃⅃ ⅲ⅃⅃ ‖ (16)

Population pyramid 'skeleton' (filled in by all students in class)

8. Each student writes in his/her homework notebook two interesting comments or observations about the population structure illustrated in the population pyramid.

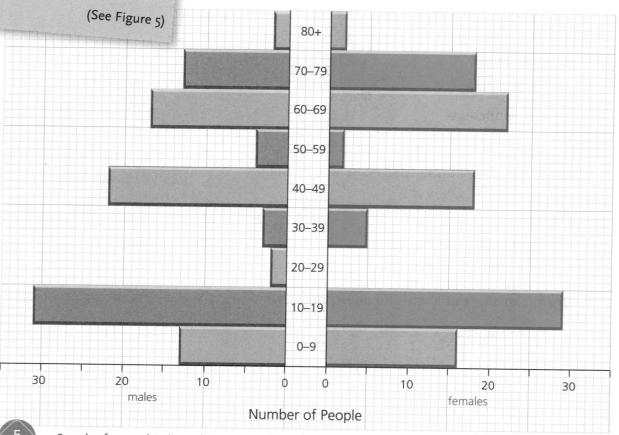

Sample of a completed population pyramid based on information in Figure 4 above.

1 Match each letter in Column X with its matching number in Column Y.

COLUMN X		COLUMN Y	
A	A person who seeks refugee status	1	A pull factor
B	A person who comes in to a country to live	2	Commuting
C	Migration from Connemara to Dublin	3	Rural to urban migration
D	A person who migrates out of a country	4	An emigrant
E	Religious, political or racial persecution	5	Attractive factor
F	Another term for 'pull factor'	6	Immigrant
G	Good job opportunities	7	Asylum seeker
H	The daily movement of people to and from work	8	Repellent factor

A	7
B	
C	
D	
E	
F	
G	
H	

 2 (a) The purple area in the graph in Figure 1 represents:

population decline ☐

overpopulation ☐

static population ☐

population increase ☐

(b) Do the migration patterns shown here suggest an improving or declining Irish economy during the period shown?

Circle the correct option.

- improving economy
- declining economy

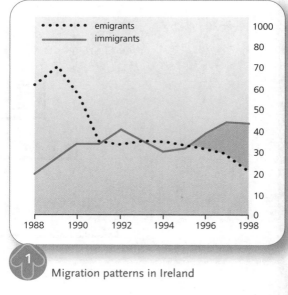

1 Migration patterns in Ireland

(c) *Briefly* explain your answer to question (b) by referring to the migration patterns shown.

_____

_____

_____

_____

Chapter 27

3 Human Migration

(a) Examine the bar chart which shows the numbers of immigrants from a selection of regions who lived in Ireland in 2002 and in 2006.

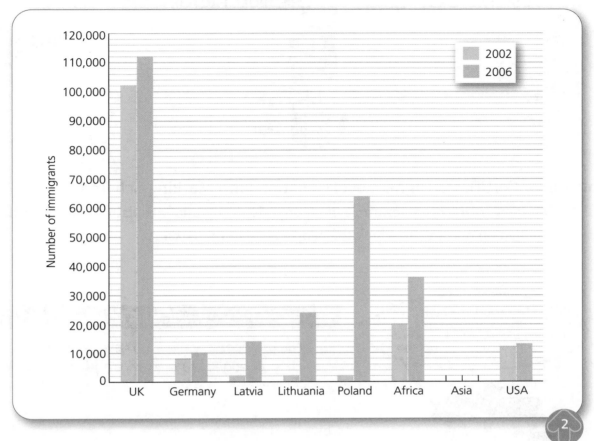

(i) From which country/region did most immigrants come in 2006?

_____

(ii) From which country/region did immigration to Ireland grow most rapidly between 2002 and 2006? _____

(iii) Calculate the increase in the number of immigrants from Lithuania to Ireland between 2002 and 2006. _____

(iv) Immigration from Asia was approximately 22,000 in 2002 and 16,000 in 2006. Draw bar charts to illustrate these figures in the appropriate spaces in Figure 2.

(b) Explain the following terms relating to human migration:

(i) Pull factors

_____

(ii) Repellent factors

_____

4 In the spaces provided, name two repellent (push) factors and two attractive (pull) factors that might cause people from overseas to migrate to Ireland.

PUSH FACTORS

1 _____

_____

2 _____

PULL FACTORS

1 _____

_____

2 _____

Sample Junior Certificate Higher Level Question with Marking Scheme

5 The *Plantation of Ulster* is an example of an organised migration. Explain three effects that this migration had on one area to which the people moved. (*9 marks*)

One effect has been written for you. Use the marking scheme provided to write full-mark answers on the other two effects.

Marking scheme

Three effects at *3 marks* each

Allocate *3 marks* as follows:

● Statement: *2 marks*
● Development: *1 mark*

Reminder:
Try to write **one extra development** in each explanation

Full-Mark Answers
(a) The planters were English-speaking Protestants. 2✓ They brought a new language and religion to Ulster. 1✓
(b)
(c)

1 The **density** of population is defined as:

the average number of people per square kilometre ☐

the total number of people in a country ☐

the number of people living in an average-sized house ☐

the age/sex structure of a rapidly growing population ☐

the extent of social inequality in a population ☐

2 Look carefully at the following table (Figure 1), taken from the **2011 Census**. It shows population change in the province of Connacht between 1986 and 2011.

Population Change in Connacht 1986–2011

	1986	1991	1996	2002	2006	2011
Galway	179,223	180,364	190,006	209,077	232,334	250,334
Leitrim	27,187	25,301	25,564	25,799	28,841	31,798
Mayo	114,985	110,713	111,497	117,446	124,684	130,638
Roscommon	54,592	51,697	51,975	53,774	58,700	63,895
Sligo	57,556	54,756	55,847	58,200	61,891	31,798

Source: CSO Census 2011

(a) Name the county with the largest population in 2011. _____

(b) Calculate the **increase** in population for County **Sligo** between 1986 and 2011.

_____

(c) Name the county which shows the **smallest change** in population between 1986 and 2011.

_____

(d) Galway is the only county which shows an increase in population each year. This was mainly because of the importance of Galway city. Mention **two** reasons why people migrate (move) to live in cities.

• _____

• _____

3 The bars in Figure 3 represent the information given in the table in Figure 2. Draw in the bars for Belgium, Ireland and Poland.

Country	Percentage change
Belgium	+5
France	+10
Italy	−9
Ireland	+36
Netherlands	+7
Poland	−12
United Kingdom	+8

Expected percentage population change between 2004 and 2050 in a number of countries

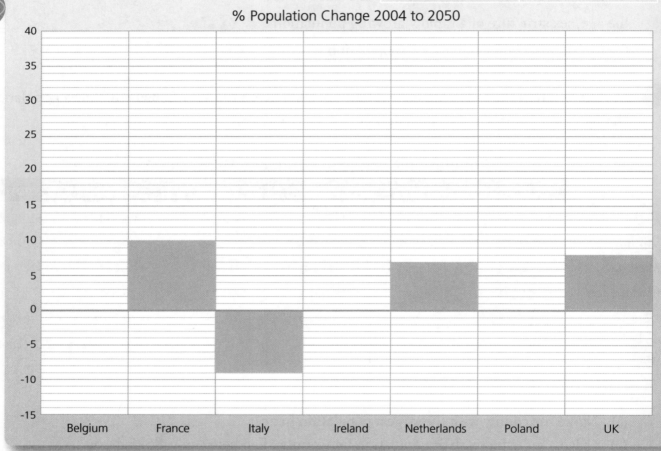

4 The following statements relate to Figures 2 and 3. Indicate whether each statement is true or false by circling the *True* or *False* alternative.

(a) The United Kingdom is expected to have a greater percentage population increase than France.   *True / False*

(b) Ireland is expected to have the highest percentage population increase of the countries named.   *True / False*

(c) France's percentage increase will be greater than those of Belgium and the Netherlands combined.   *True / False*

(d) Poland's population will decrease by three per cent more than will that of Italy.   *True / False*

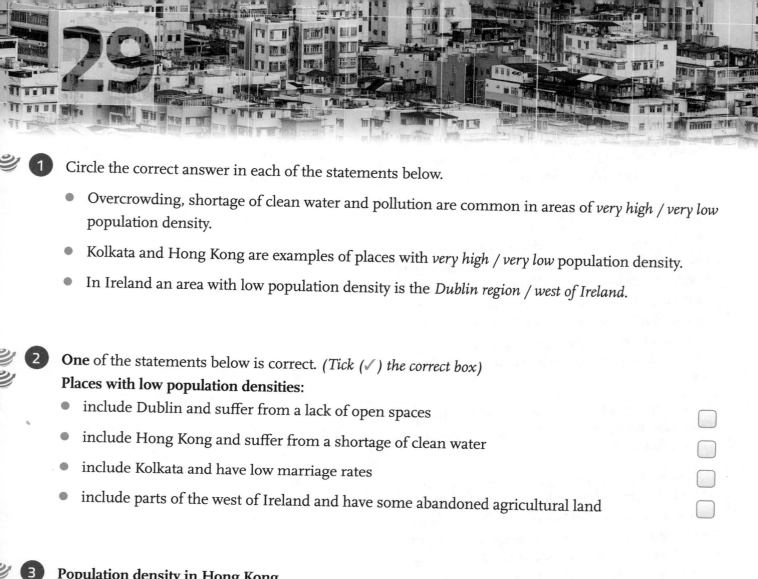

1 Circle the correct answer in each of the statements below.

- Overcrowding, shortage of clean water and pollution are common in areas of *very high / very low* population density.

- Kolkata and Hong Kong are examples of places with *very high / very low* population density.

- In Ireland an area with low population density is the *Dublin region / west of Ireland.*

2 **One** of the statements below is correct. *(Tick (✓) the correct box)*
Places with low population densities:

- include Dublin and suffer from a lack of open spaces ☐

- include Hong Kong and suffer from a shortage of clean water ☐

- include Kolkata and have low marriage rates ☐

- include parts of the west of Ireland and have some abandoned agricultural land ☐

3 **Population density in Hong Kong**
Indicate which **three** statements below are correct by ticking (✓) the correct box.

1. Hong Kong has a low population density.

2. Air pollution from traffic is a big problem.

3. The harbour waters are heavily polluted.

4. Hong Kong has plenty of open spaces.

5. Many of the people live in high-rise apartments.

| 1, 3, 4 ☐ | 1, 4, 5 ☐ |
| 2, 3, 5 ☐ | 3, 4, 5 ☐ |

Rural depopulation in Loughfadda

Seventy-year-old BJ Sullivan looked out over the beautiful but partially abandoned hill slopes of his native Loughfadda.

Ancient fields clung to the lower levels of the rocky hill. But many had been abandoned by farm animals and crops. Some had been planted with conifers while others were being conquered by furze and heather. Three traditional farmhouses were strung along the base of the nearby hill. One was in ruins. Another – just above the shore of a long, narrow glacial lake – was being converted into a holiday home by a family from Galway City.

'The land here needs young people,' said BJ wistfully. 'Old fellows like me no longer have the strength or the energy to work it.'

BJ explained that many young people had left the area for the third-level colleges, jobs and social life offered by cities such as Galway and Dublin. Since the economic collapse of 2008, many more had emigrated to the UK and Australia. The effects of this on Loughfadda have been many and negative. The local post office closed two years ago. The local GAA club had to amalgamate with another neighbouring club. The two surviving shops in the village are struggling to survive. It has been over a year since a wedding was celebrated at the local church.

'A factory or other industry would work wonders in this locality,' said BJ. 'But sure there is little or no chance of that.'

Use material from the simulated newspaper extract provided or your own knowledge to answer the questions below.

(a) Name three reasons why people migrate from some rural areas in Ireland.

- _____
- _____
- _____

(b) Name three consequences (effects) on rural areas of out-migration.

- _____
- _____
- _____

(c) Suggest three reasons why industry might not be attracted to rural areas such as Loughfadda.

- _____
- _____
- _____

Chapter 29

5 The country shown in colour in Figure 1 has a very low human population density.

(a) Name the country.

_____

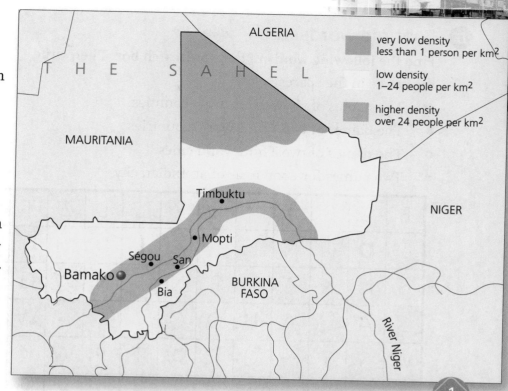

- ALGERIA
- very low density less than 1 person per km²
- low density 1–24 people per km²
- higher density over 24 people per km²
- THE SAHEL
- MAURITANIA
- Timbuktu
- NIGER
- Mopti
- Ségou
- San
- Bamako
- Bia
- BURKINA FASO
- River Niger

1

(b) With the help of the map attempt to explain *why* population density is higher in the 'higher density' part of the country shown than it is in the 'low density' part of the country.

_____

_____

_____

_____

_____

(c) Describe *two* problems caused by low population density that affect the country shown.

- _____

_____

_____

_____

- _____

_____

_____

_____

_____

6 Funtime wordsearch

Find the following words in the **wordsearch box**. Then write
the words in the spaces below.

- The names of six Western Irish counties
- The names of two Third World countries
- The names of two Third world cities
- Two names for poor areas of an Indian city.

These words could appear left to right, right to left, top to bottom or bottom to top in the wordsearch box.

B	A	B	T	Y	W	X	L	L	Z	T	B	A	H	**B**	Z	E
O	**D**	O	N	E	G	A	**L**	B	M	F	G	**C**	N	A	P	N
S	N	K	A	M	P	N	E	N	W	G	N	L	J	M	K	O
S	A	C	A	**U**	O	Q	I	Y	A	W	L	A	**G**	A	U	M
W	S	T	N	G	R	W	T	P	W	K	U	R	P	K	X	M
T	E	R	B	A	T	S	R	B	Y	R	R	E	K	O	B	O
Z	E	G	N	N	O	G	I	L	**S**	X	B	Z	R	E	U	C
U	T	M	L	D	V	U	**M**	A	Y	O	G	X	T	W	L	S
G	S	T	E	A	**S**	H	A	N	T	Y	T	O	W	N	S	O
L	U	E	E	H	B	H	H	J	A	I	D	N	**I**	S	O	R
M	**B**	N	T	C	H	A	L	L	Y	A	T	A	K	L	O	**K**

Six western Irish counties:

1. _____   2. _____   3. _____

4. _____   5. _____   6. _____

Two Third World countries:

1. _____   2. _____

Two Third World cities:

1. _____   2. _____

Two names for poor areas in an Indian city:

1. _____   2. _____

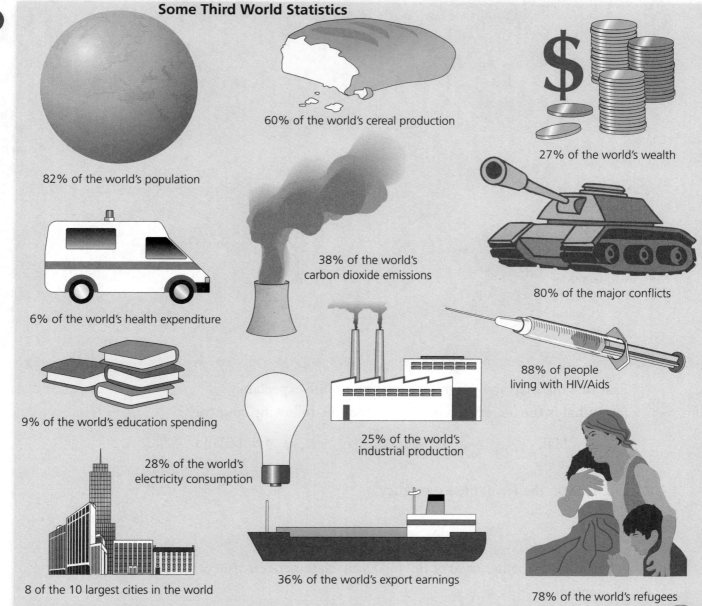

Some Third World Statistics

82% of the world's population

60% of the world's cereal production

27% of the world's wealth

6% of the world's health expenditure

38% of the world's carbon dioxide emissions

80% of the major conflicts

9% of the world's education spending

88% of people living with HIV/Aids

28% of the world's electricity consumption

25% of the world's industrial production

8 of the 10 largest cities in the world

36% of the world's export earnings

78% of the world's refugees

The following statements all relate to Figure 1. Not all the statements are true.

Identify the set of true statements by ticking (✓) the correct box.

1. The Third World contains more than three-quarters of the world's people.
2. Twenty per cent of the world's ten largest cities are in the South.
3. Three-quarters of the world's industrial production is NOT in the South.
4. Less than one-tenth of the world's health expenditure is in the Third World.
5. Slightly less than three-quarters of all people living with Aids are in the South.

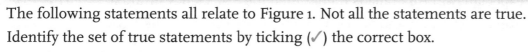

1, 2, 3 ☐   1, 3, 4 ☐   2, 3, 4 ☐   2, 4, 5 ☐

2 **World life expectancy**

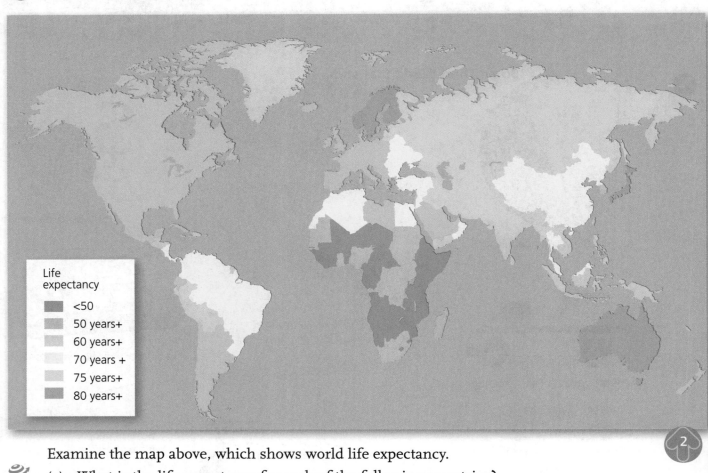

Life expectancy
- ▓ <50
- ▓ 50 years+
- ▓ 60 years+
- ▓ 70 years +
- ▓ 75 years+
- ▓ 80 years+

Examine the map above, which shows world life expectancy.

(a) What is the life expectancy for each of the following countries?

- Mali _____
- Ireland _____

(b) Explain the term 'life expectancy'.

_____

(c) Indicate whether each of the following statements is true or false by circling the *True* or *False* option:

   (i)   Life expectancy in Australia is higher than life expectancy in Brazil.   *True / False*

   (ii) Life expectancy in Ireland is lower than life expectancy in the USA.   *True / False*

(d) Explain two reasons why life expectancy is higher in Ireland than in countries such as Mali.

   (i) _____

   _____

   (ii) _____

Chapter 30

3 The statements that follow all relate to the bar graphs in Figure 3. Which set of statements are correct? *Tick (✓) the correct box.*

1. All areas shown display a decrease over time in under-five mortality rate.
2. Developed regions showed the greatest decrease in infant mortality.
3. Sub-Saharan Africa showed a decrease of 69 (deaths per 1,000 live births).
4. Southern Asia halved its under-five mortality rate between 1990 and 2011.
5. Child mortality in the world as a whole was 51 in 2011.

1, 2, 4 ☐   1, 2, 5 ☐   1, 3, 5 ☐   2, 3, 5 ☐

3 Under-five mortality rate in various regions in 1990 and in 2011

4 **Know your places!**

Match the number of each place in Column 1 with the letter of its corresponding description in Column 2. These places have featured in Chapters 25 to 30. One match has been made for you in the grid provided.

COLUMN 1		COLUMN 2			
1	Bamako	A	Includes Japan and Russia	1	
2	Fingal	B	North Dublin	2	B
3	Fermanagh	C	Brazilian city	3	
4	Sao Paolo	D	Ulster Plantation town	4	
5	Kampala	E	County planted around 1609	5	
6	Milan	F	Part of Hong Kong	6	
7	The North	G	Kolkata shanty towns	7	
8	Enniskillen	H	Capital city of Mali	8	
9	Bustees	I	Capital city of Uganda	9	
10	Po	J	North Italian city	10	
11	Kowloon	K	River in Northern Italy	11	

1 (a) Examine the map in Figure 1, which shows Norman towns in Ireland. These towns are situated mainly in which of the following parts of the country?

Tick (✓) the correct box.

- The North and East ☐
- The South and East ☐
- The North and West ☐
- The South and West ☐

(b) Give *two reasons* why most Norman towns were located in the parts of the country you identified in question (a) above.

- _____
- _____
- _____

- _____
- _____

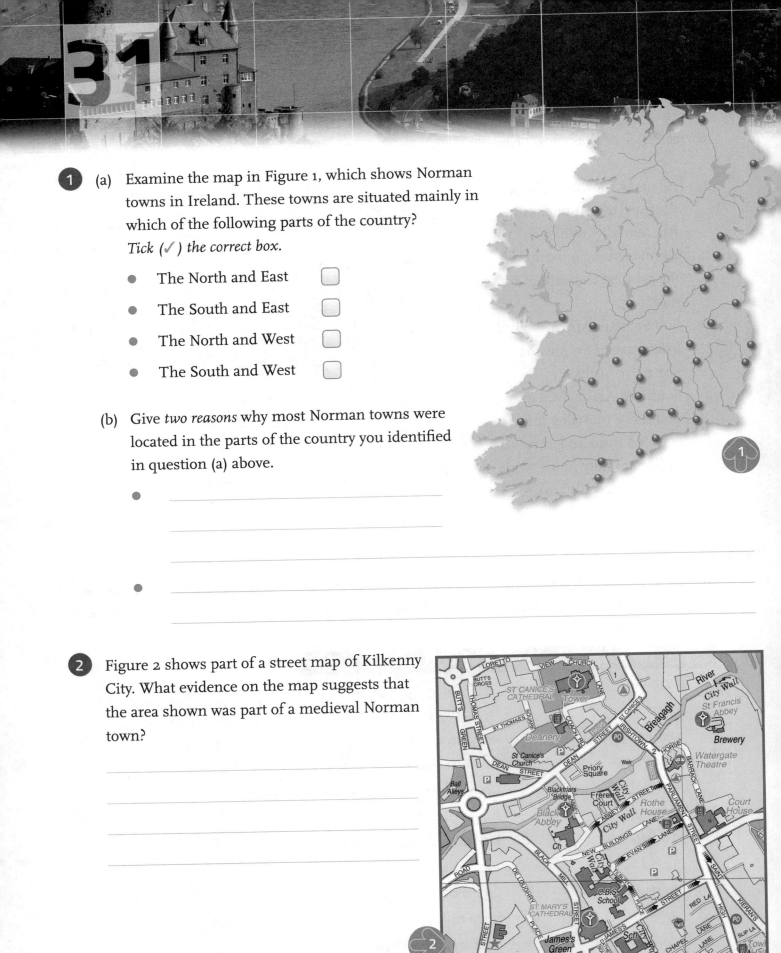

2 Figure 2 shows part of a street map of Kilkenny City. What evidence on the map suggests that the area shown was part of a medieval Norman town?

- _____
- _____
- _____
- _____

3 Match the number of each item in Column 1 with its matching lettered item in Column 2.

COLUMN 1	
1	How settlements are 'arranged'
2	Locations of coastal Viking towns
3	Locations of early Norman towns in Leinster
4	Settlements along an important road
5	When no particular pattern exists

COLUMN 2	
A	Linear pattern
B	Dispersed pattern
C	Settlement pattern
D	Random pattern
E	Linear pattern

1	
2	
3	B
4	
5	

4 The map in Figure 3 shows the locations of some Irish towns.

(a) Are these towns distributed in a generally *nucleated, ribboned* or *dispersed* pattern?

_____

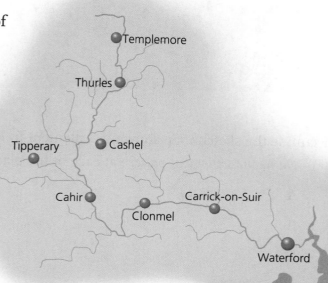

(b) Explain in one sentence *why* these settlements are distributed in the pattern you identified in (a) above.

_____

_____

(c) Which of the settlements shown is at the lowest bridging point of the River Suir?

_____

(d) Why are important settlements often located at the lowest bridging points of rivers?

_____

_____

_____

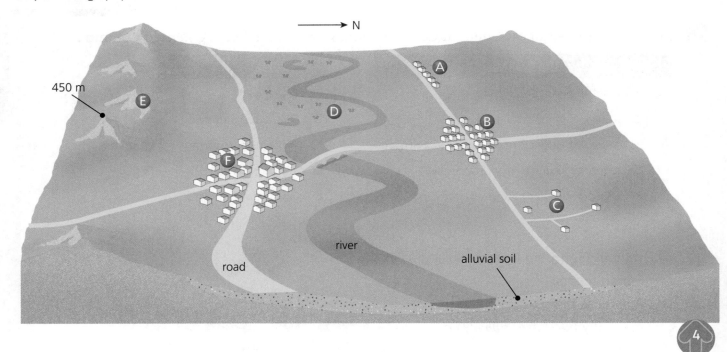

4

5 Examine the sketch map showing settlement in Figure 4 above.
(a) *Name the settlement pattern* at each of the places labelled **A**, **B** and **C** on the sketch map.

A _____

B _____

C _____

(b) Give one reason why there is no settlement at the place labelled **D**.

_____

(c) Give two reasons why there is no settlement at **E**.

(i) _____

(ii) _____

(d) Give *two explanations* why the town labelled F may have developed where it did.

(i) _____

_____

_____

(ii) _____

_____

_____

6 Examine the map of a European country in Figure 5. Indicate whether each of the statements below is true or false by circling the *True* or *False* option.

(a) The country dominating the map is Belgium.
True / False

(b) The area labelled 'W' is an example of a polder.
True / False

(c) The River Rhine flows generally westwards through the country.
True / False

(d) The area labelled 'X' is the North East Polder.
True / False

(e) The map shows that the River Rhine flows through part of Germany.
True / False

(f) Part of Germany is shown on the southwest of the map.
True / False

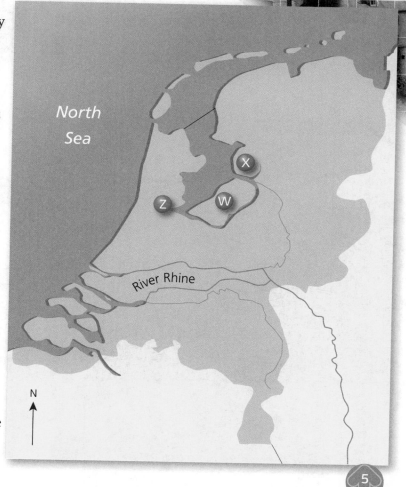

5

7 Examine Figure 6.
Circle the *correct option* in each of the following statements:

(a) Germany is famous for its polder landscape.
True / False

(b) A country that has reclaimed much land from the sea is
The Netherlands / Mali.

(c) Planned farms are evident in the Dutch polders. *True / False*

(d) The overall settlement pattern shown in Figure 6 is *linear /dispersed / nucleated.*

(e) The 'ditches' labelled in Figure 6 are *raised field boundaries / drainage channels and field boundaries*

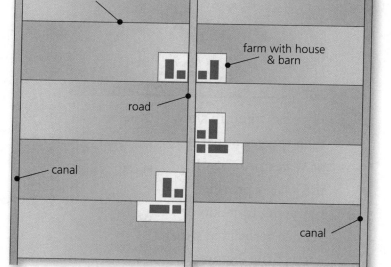

6

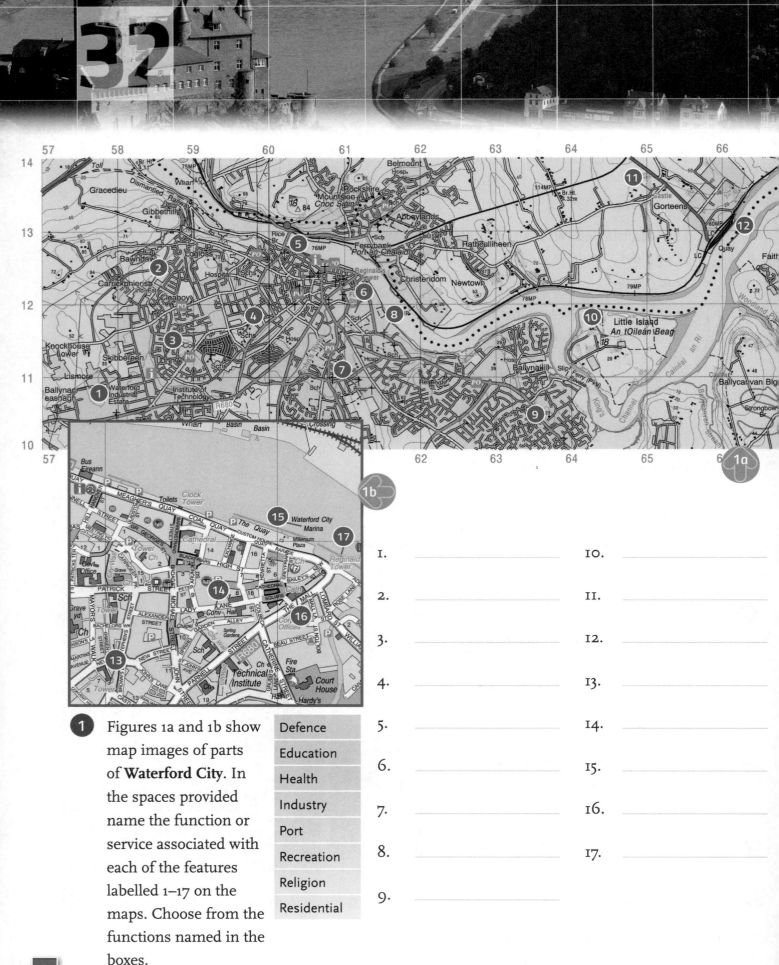

1 Figures 1a and 1b show map images of parts of **Waterford City**. In the spaces provided name the function or service associated with each of the features labelled 1–17 on the maps. Choose from the functions named in the boxes.

Defence

Education

Health

Industry

Port

Recreation

Religion

Residential

1. _____   10. _____

2. _____   11. _____

3. _____   12. _____

4. _____   13. _____

5. _____   14. _____

6. _____   15. _____

7. _____   16. _____

8. _____   17. _____

9. _____

Chapter 32

2 In the spaces provided, describe three functions of *Limerick City* and three functions of *Köln*. Use the marking scheme given below to guide you.

Marking Scheme

Each function is awarded *four marks*, which are allocated as follows:

- Naming the function = *1 mark*
- Development = *2 marks*
- Example or other development = *1 mark*

*Try to write **one extra** development for each description*

For Example: 1 ✓

Limerick has a major residential function.

Many of its people now live in suburbs at
2 ✓ 1 ✓
the edges of the city. Ballynanty is an

example of such a suburb. 4/4

Limerick City	Köln
1.	1.
2.	2.
3.	3.

3 'Rivers have a big influence on the development of settlements.'
With reference to an Irish or European river basin you have studied, discuss two ways in which the river has influenced the development of settlement in this area.

(a) _____

_____

_____

_____

_____

_____

(b) _____

_____

_____

_____

_____

_____

4 Link each of the letters in column X with its matching number in column Y.

	COLUMN X		COLUMN Y		
A	Were once the locations of agricultural fairs	1	Villages	A	
B	May have beaches, golf courses, tourist information centres, etc.	2	Market towns	B	
C	Cater for very limited everyday services	3	Defence towns	C	
D	May have developed originally around monasteries or cathedrals	4	Ports	D	
E	Are situated in deep harbours with good docking facilities	5	Dormitory towns	E	
F	Most of their inhabitants are employed in nearby cities	6	Recreational towns	F	
G	May still have the remains of castles or old town walls	7	Ecclesiastical towns	G	

1 In the grid provided, link each of the features or characteristics in Column X with its matching town function in Column Y. One match has been made for you.

COLUMN X (features or characteristics)		COLUMN Y (town functions)			
A	Castles	1	Ecclesiastical	A	
B	Fertile agricultural hinterland*	2	Market	B	
C	Mineral resources	3	Manufacturing	C	
D	Cathedrals and churches	4	Defence	D	1
E	Sheltered harbour	5	Mining	E	
F	Industrial estate	6	Port	F	

*hinterland = surrounding area

2 Which of the following statements are true?

1. The functions of towns may change over time.

2. Towns such as Navan and Leixlip are multifunctional.

3. People often commute between dormitory towns and nearby cities where they work.

4. Navan is a mining town in Co. Cavan.

5. Intel and Dell are multinational companies with factories in Leixlip.

6. Manufacturing is Leixlip's main source of employment.

The correct statements are:

1, 2, 4 and 5 ☐   1, 2, 3 and 5 ☐   1, 2, 3 and 6 ☐   2, 3, 4 and 6 ☐

Tick (✓) the correct box.

3 **The functions of many towns have changed over time.**

In the case of one named Irish town or city that you have studied, describe how its functions have changed. In your answer refer to three different functions.

_____

_____

_____

_____

_____

_____

_____

_____

_____

_____

_____

_____

_____

_____

_____

_____

_____

_____

_____

_____

_____

> Use this marking scheme to help you with your answer

Marking Scheme

Naming the town or city = *1 mark*
Three functions at 3 marks each
Allocate each 3 marks as follows:

Clear statement/name function	= *1 mark*
Development	= *1 mark*
Another development	= *1 mark*
Total	**= 10 marks**

Investigate, Share, Discuss and Display

- Each student should try to investigate past and present functions of the town in which your school is located.
- Students should share their findings in a class discussion on how functions of the town have changed over time. Pictures, maps, Google searches, evidence of older people, etc. might all be used to contribute to the discussion.
- A wall-chart on past and present functions of your town might then be prepared and displayed.

1 Link each of the letters in Column X with its matching number in Column Y. One match has been made for you.

COLUMN X	
A	*Rhine-Rhone* and *Main-Danube*
B	The main hub (meeting place) of Irish road and rail routes
C	Called 'the main road of Germany'
D	Location of Ireland's principal airport
E	Used to reduce congestion in urban areas
F	A County Clare airport

COLUMN Y	
1	Ring roads
2	Rhine
3	Shannon
4	Dublin
5	Canals
6	Dublin

A	
B	
C	
D	
E	1
F	

2 Indicate whether each of the statements below is *true* or *false* by circling the correct *alternative* in each case.

(a) The Rhine rises in Switzerland, flows through much of Germany and enters the North Sea in the Netherlands.　　　*True / False*

(b) The Rhine has its source in the Netherlands and much of its course in Germany.　　　*True / False*

(c) The Upper Rhine is in Switzerland and the Lower Rhine is in the Netherlands.　　　*True / False*

(d) In general, ships and barges carry industrial goods up the Rhine and raw materials down the Rhine to the North Sea.　　　*True / False*

(e) Port cities in the Netherlands, Germany and Switzerland are all linked by Rhine water transport.　　　*True / False*

(f) Shannon is Ireland's largest airport.　　　*True / False*

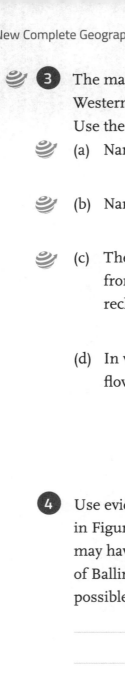

3 The map on the right shows a part of Western Europe.

Use the map to answer the questions below:

(a) Name the river labelled 'X' on the map.

_____

(b) Name the country labelled 'Y'.

_____

(c) The place labelled 'Z' has been reclaimed from the sea. The name given to land reclaimed from the sea is:

_____

(d) In which general direction does River X flow through country Y?

_____

4 Use evidence from the Ordnance Survey map in Figure 2 to explain how transport links may have contributed over time to the growth of Ballinasloe, Co. Galway. Refer to three possible transport links.

_____

_____

_____

_____

_____

_____

_____

_____

_____

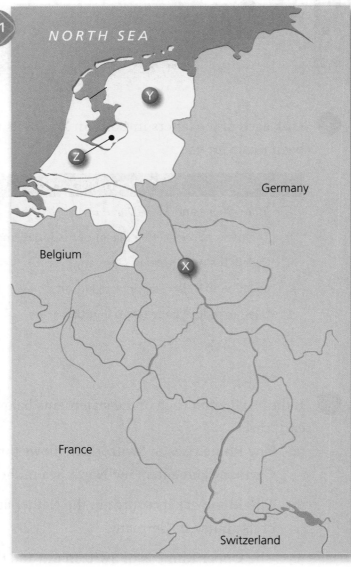

Chapter 34

5 Revision Fun Exercise on Chapters 31–34

On the spaces provided, write the word that fits each of the descriptions 1–14 below. You can check that your answers are correct by finding and highlighting each word in the Word Search grid in Figure 3.

1. Defensive feature in Norman town ___ ___ ___ ___ ___

2. Norman town in Co. Meath ___ ___ ___ ___

3. Ireland's primate city ___ ___ ___ ___ ___ ___

4. Rivers on which ships can travel ___ ___ ___ ___ ___ ___ ___ ___

5. Land reclaimed from the sea ___ ___ ___ ___ ___

6. English King/Limerick castle ___ ___ ___ ___

7. Famous Limerick museum ___ ___ ___ ___

8. Rhine's largest port ___ ___ ___ ___ ___ ___ ___

9. Swiss river port ___ ___ ___ ___ ___

10. Co. Meath mining town ___ ___ ___ ___ ___

11. Manufacturing company in Leixlip ___ ___ ___ ___

12. Major port on River Main ___ ___ ___ ___ ___ ___ ___ ___ ___

13. Also called a satellite town ___ ___ ___ ___ ___ ___ ___ ___

14. Town and airport ___ ___ ___ ___ ___ ___

The first letter of each word hidden is printed in BLACK.

W	E	V	T	Y	U	A	I	O	U	T	S	B	S	W	T	N	B	M	I	R	T	V	X	Z
C	A	B	X	R	V	M	M	I	N	T	E	L	P	N	W	D	V	G	X	D	X	Y	V	I
A	A	W	A	O	T	B	Z	R	E	D	L	O	P	C	V	F	P	L	B	J	Q	F	D	T
S	B	H	H	T	P	D	R	E	S	N	B	K	I	J	P	C	P	F	A	E	I	N	W	W
T	A	V	R	I	D	H	N	C	F	R	A	N	K	F	U	R	T	W	S	D	V	A	V	W
L	R	C	L	M	F	Q	F	E	R	M	G	X	H	Z	F	M	Z	F	E	J	Q	V	S	S
E	C	P	G	R	T	D	K	J	I	G	I	D	Z	E	R	O	T	T	L	R	D	A	M	S
Y	S	O	T	O	N	G	N	C	L	S	V	X	C	H	R	Q	S	S	H	A	N	N	O	N
W	U	X	Z	D	U	B	L	I	N	M	A	Q	L	R	F	C	L	G	H	D	I	M	M	X
P	N	M	S	R	H	F	O	I	T	V	N	H	O	J	K	O	O	M	V	X	P	O	M	L

3 Word search

6 Giant Revision Wordgame for Chapters 32 to 34

Clues Down

A. The source of the River Rhine is in this country.

B. People live in this type of town but work in a nearby city.

Clues Across

1. Might be evidence of an old defence town.
2. Munster city
3. Area surrounding a settlement – see page 105 of this Skills Book
4. Another word for Clue B Down
5. German for 'confluence' and a city on the Rhine
6. Big Leixlip manufacturer
7. Large lake on the River Shannon
8. The Main-Danube is one
9. Tributary that joins the Rhine at Koblenz
10. Home of the Dutch
11. Ports like Dublin have them
12. Important market, port and recreational city on the Rhine
13. An Irish settlement with a co-operative mart would have this function
14. *Sounds* like the principal tributary of the Rhine
15. City at the lowest bridge point of the Shannon
16. Europe's largest port
17. Town on the Shannon below Lough Ree
18. These people developed Limerick City in medieval times
19. Might be found in a settlement with an old ecclesiastical function

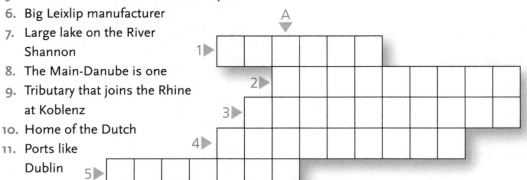
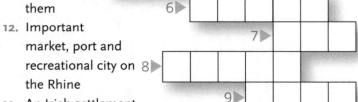
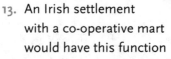
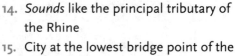
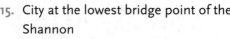
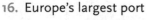
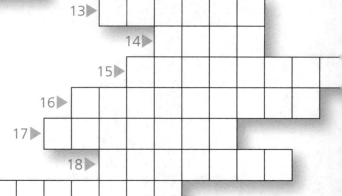

1 The map in Figure 1 shows the growth of Dublin.

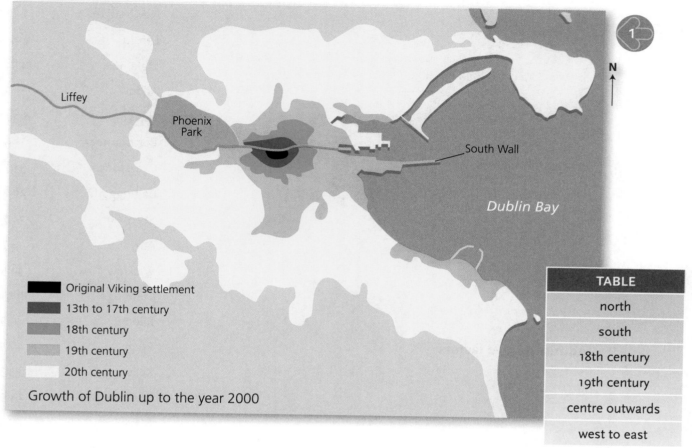

Growth of Dublin up to the year 2000

Legend:
- Original Viking settlement
- 13th to 17th century
- 18th century
- 19th century
- 20th century

TABLE
north
south
18th century
19th century
centre outwards
west to east

Use the **map** to complete the paragraph below using items from the **table** above.

The map shows that Dublin grew outwards from a Viking settlement that developed on the

_____ side of the River Liffey. It extended to the South Wall in the _____

century. Dublin's period of most rapid growth was during the _____ century. Over its

history, Dublin grew generally from the _____.

2 Examine Figure 2 on the next page, which is a table of Ireland's fastest-growing urban centres (excluding Dublin).

(a) On the spaces provided, put in rank order the **four** fastest growing urban centres.

(b) With reference to **one** Irish urban centre that you have studied, explain the factors that led to its development. Use the headings shown in the answer spaces given.

3 Figure 2 shows the percentage change in population in a selection of towns between 1981 and 1996.

Part (a): Rankings

1. _____

2. _____

3. _____

4. _____

Part (b):

● **Economic factors**

_____

_____

_____

_____

● **Administrative factors**

_____

_____

_____

_____

● **Social factors**

_____

_____

_____

_____

_____

CENTRE	CHANGE %
Bray	22.2
Lucan	–
Swords	100.3
Navan	15.0
Newbridge	24.7
Leixlip	44.5
Malahide	47.8
Arklow	-1.0
Naas	68.7
Portmarnock	11.4
Greystones	34.3
Balbriggan	26.3
Skerries	26.7
Athy	-4.7
Wicklow	36.5
Celbridge	168.1
Kildare	6.5
Rush	40.5
Kells	-3.3
Trim	24.9
Maynooth	151.7
Ashbourne	115.0

2

Marking Scheme

(a) (*4 marks*): Allow *one mark* each for four urban centres identified and ranked correctly.

(b) (*12 marks*): Allow *four marks* for each of three headings. Allocate each *four marks* as follows:
Opening statement/point = *2m*
A second statement or development = *1m*
Another statement = *1m*

Chapter 35

4 The two maps show the growth of Dublin between 1936 and 1988.

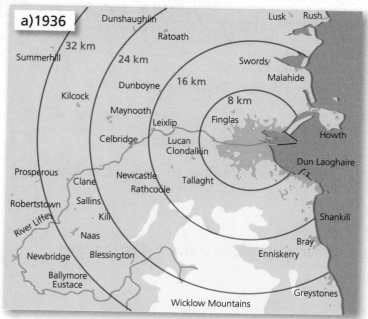

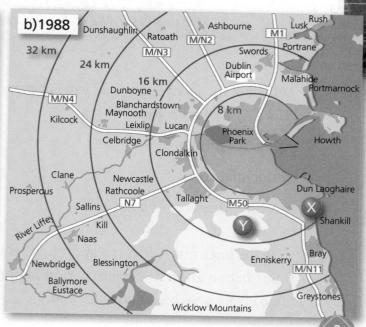

With reference to one or both of the maps:

● Suggest **one** reason for the rapid growth of Dublin at the place labelled X.

● Suggest **one** reason for the less rapid development of Dublin at the place labelled Y.

5 Which of the following statements best describes the information shown in the cartoon?
(a) Dublin City is constantly attracting new residents from outlying areas.
(b) Dublin City looks like a saucer-shaped depression.
(c) New towns outside Dublin have taken the overspill population from the city.
(d) Tallaght is continually decreasing in population size.
Tick (✓) the correct box.

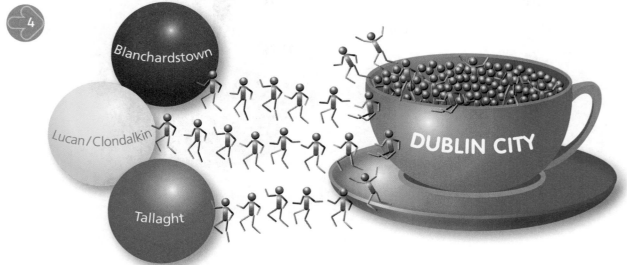

1 Which of the following would you *not* expect to find in a typical Western city?
Tick (✓) the correct box.

industrial areas ☐   a number of shopping centres ☐

residential areas ☐   many houses built in an unplanned way ☐

a central core area of business ☐

2 Use the lines numbered 1, 2 and 3 to label the divided rectangle in Figure 1. Refer to the information given in the pie chart in Figure 2.
Two labels have been added for you.

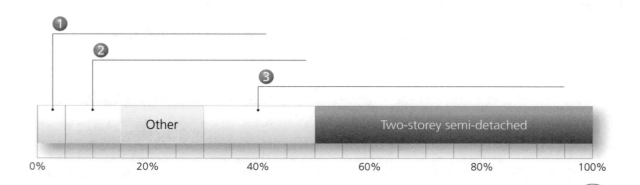

① ② ③

| Other | | Two-storey semi-detached |

0%   20%   40%   60%   80%   100%

1

● Two-storey semi-detached

● Two-storey detached

● Bungalow

● Terrace

● Other

5%
10%
15%
50%
20%

2

3 The diagram in Figure 3 shows seven numbered functional areas in an imaginary city. These areas are labelled 1–7.

(a) On the **grid** provided link each number with the correct function.

(b) Each of the three **pictures** given below shows one of the urban functions named in the grid. Write this urban function on the space provided with each picture.

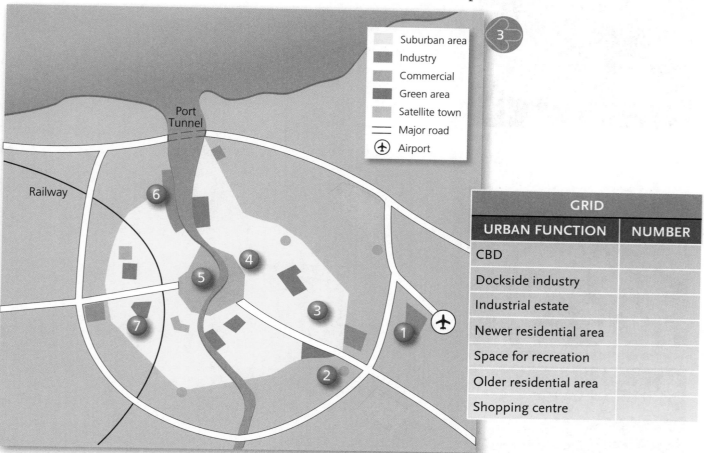

GRID	
URBAN FUNCTION	**NUMBER**
CBD	
Dockside industry	
Industrial estate	
Newer residential area	
Space for recreation	
Older residential area	
Shopping centre	

Map legend:
- Suburban area
- Industry
- Commercial
- Green area
- Satellite town
- Major road
- Airport

4 Photographs **A** to **D** show different urban functions. Name and describe each function.

A _____
_____
_____
_____
_____

B _____
_____
_____
_____
_____

C _____
_____
_____
_____
_____

D _____
_____
_____
_____
_____

⑤ Drawing a sketch map – a picture memory class exercise

This exercise is designed to help you to focus on and to remember information by drawing pictures or sketches.

This exercise should take about fifteen minutes. To do it you will need a pencil and a clean sheet of paper. The subject of the exercise is 'Functional zones in an imaginary city'.

First your teacher should write the following on the whiteboard. Try to show these in your sketch or picture:

- Roads
- Airport
- CBD
- Public park
- Industrial zone
- Main residential areas

What you should do in four steps:

1. Your teacher will slowly and clearly read aloud three times the extract in Figure 4.

   While your teacher reads aloud, close your eyes and focus on what is being read. Keep your Skills Book closed. Do not draw, write or say anything while your teacher is reading.

2. With your Skills Book closed, draw a picture or sketch to illustrate what your teacher has read. You may label your picture/sketch if you wish.

3. You will have only two minutes to complete the picture/sketch. You must therefore work quickly. Do not worry about neatness or 'artistic merit'.

4. Swap your completed drawing with the student sitting closest to you. Record how many of the urban zones and features your 'partner' showed correctly in his/her drawing before taking back your own picture. You may open your Skills Book and consult the extract in Figure 4 while you are doing this part of the exercise.

Functional Zones in an Imaginary City

- Assume that north is on the top of your drawing. East is to the right. West is to the left.
- This is a small oval-shaped city, surrounded by an outer ring road. Two major roads cross in the centre of the city. One road runs east–west and the other runs north–south. These roads dissect the outer ring road.
- There is an airport to the east of the ring road, close to where it meets the east–west main road.
- The CBD is at the city centre. It contains some very tall buildings, including one or two 'skyscrapers'.
- West of the CBD is a large rectangular public park.
- There is an industrial zone close to the airport on the east side of the city.
- The city's most expensive residential zone is in the north-west of the city. Dwellings there are mainly large, detached houses.
- A large middle-to-lower-income residential area covers the south-eastern quarter of the city.

4

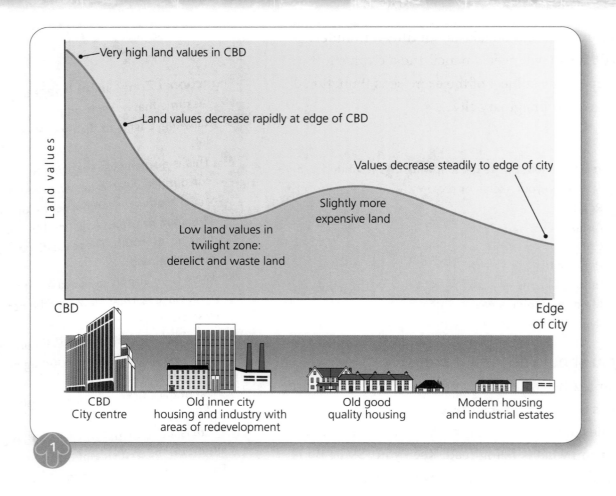

Very high land values in CBD

Land values decrease rapidly at edge of CBD

Values decrease steadily to edge of city

Slightly more expensive land

Low land values in twilight zone: derelict and waste land

Land values

CBD

Edge of city

CBD City centre

Old inner city housing and industry with areas of redevelopment

Old good quality housing

Modern housing and industrial estates

1 Study the diagram, which shows a cross-section of a city.
You are required to identify which *three* of these statements are correct.

1. Land values in the city centre are very high.

2. Land values are lowest at the edge of the city.

3. Two-storey buildings are found mainly in the city centre.

4. Values rise in the zone of modern housing and industrial estates.

5. In the old inner city land values are relatively low.

The *correct* statements are numbers:

1, 3, 5 ☐   1, 2, 5 ☐   2, 3, 4 ☐   3, 4, 5 ☐

2 Examine the photograph below and answer the following questions.

(a) In which of the city zones **A**, **B** or **C** would land values be highest? _____

(b) State **two** reasons why land values are highest in this zone.

  • _____
     _____
     _____

  • _____
     _____
     _____

(c) How do very high land values affect the types and uses of urban buildings?

_____
_____
_____
_____

3 (a) Examine the photographs below and name each housing type, by writing the correct answer in the spaces provided.

A _____ B _____ C _____

(b) In which of the following urban zones are the houses in photograph **C** most likely to be found? *Tick (✓) the correct box.*

the CBD ☐   the inner city ☐   the suburbs ☐   an industrial estate ☐

(c) Which of the three photographs shows the most intensive residential land use and which shows the least intensive residential land use?

Most intensive _____   Least intensive _____

(d) Circle the correct **alternatives** in the statement below:
*'The oldest houses are shown in photograph **A/B/C** and these houses are likely to be found closer to / further away from the city centre than the other houses shown.'*

4 In cities in developed countries:

- land values generally increase as you go out of the city centre to the suburbs ☐

- new industrial estates are mostly built near the city centre ☐

- the average height of buildings generally increases as you go towards the city centre ☐

- detached houses are most common in the Central Business District (CBD) ☐

- houses tend to be old in the outer suburbs of cities ☐
Tick (✓) the correct box.

5 Examine the photographs of Irish urban dwellings labelled **A** to **E**. The statements below relate to these photographs. Indicate whether each statement is true or false by circling the *True* or *False* option.

(a) The lowest density dwelling is shown in photograph A.
True / False

(b) The houses in photograph C are older than those in photograph E.
True / False

(c) The house in photograph A has more floor space than has a house in photograph C.
True / False

(d) The houses in photograph D are in an area of lower density than those in photograph E.
True / False

(e) The houses in photograph C are likely to be nearer to the city centre than those in photograph E.
True / False

(f) Housing densities are highest in the dwellings shown in photograph C.
True / False

(g) The houses in photograph D appear to have been built by a city council or other public authority.
True / False

(h) Land values in photograph A are lower than those in photograph D.
True / False

(i) Houses in photograph E are likely to be located in an inner city area.
True / False

1 Examine the map of Dublin's DART lines in Figure 1.

 (a) If you boarded the DART at Dún Laoghaire station and travelled northwards for seven stations, what station would you be at?

_____

(b) Imagine that somebody in Malahide asked you how to get to Howth using the DART system. Respond to this request, mentioning any possible line-change involved in the journey.

_____

_____

_____

_____

_____

_____

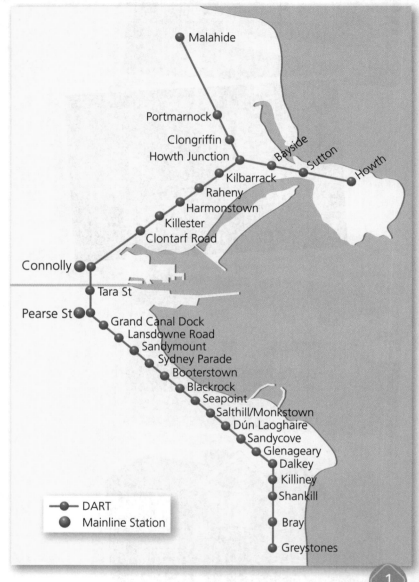

 2 **Traffic in an Irish city**

TIME PERIOD	9 a.m. to 10 a.m.	11 a.m. to 12 noon	2 p.m. to 3 p.m.	5 p.m. to 6 p.m.
Bicycles	20	8	17	23
Cars	403	350	260	578
Trucks	79	58	35	89

The table above shows the results of a traffic survey carried out by a group of students.

(a) What was the number of trucks counted between 9 a.m. and 10 a.m.? _____

(b) What was the total number of bicycles counted during the survey? _____

(c) State **one** reason for the larger number of cars counted between 5 p.m. and 6 p.m.

_____

_____

(d) Explain two reasons why traffic congestion happens in our towns and cities.

- _____

_____

- _____

_____

(e) Explain **two** solutions to traffic congestion.

_____

_____

_____

_____

3

What urban problem is referred to in the cartoon in Figure 3 and what point is the cartoon making about that problem?

- Problem: _____

- Point being made: _____

4 Study the diagram in Figure 4, which shows percentage increases in the time it took to travel to Dublin City betwen 1990 and 2006.

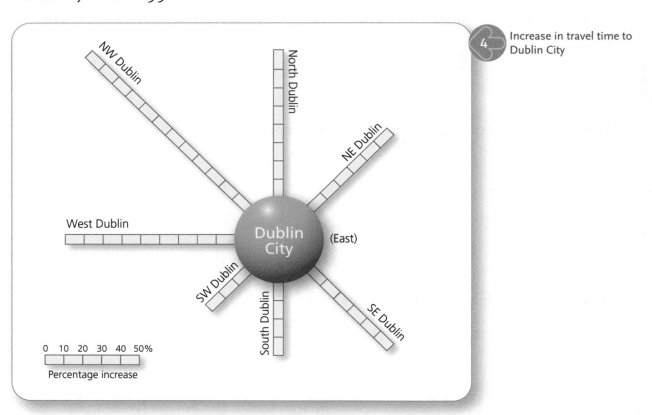

(a) Name, **in rank order**, the three areas worst affected by the increase in travel times.

(i) _____

(ii) _____

(iii) _____

(b) What is the percentage increase in travel time to the city from north-east Dublin?

_____

(c) Why do you think no increase in travel time is recorded from the east?

_____

(d) Explain two actions that could be taken to reduce delays in travel time in and out of Dublin.

(i) _____

_____

(ii) _____

5 (a) The bar graph in Figure 5 shows the number of vehicles that entered and left an Irish settlement on a certain day. Complete the bar graphs so as to show **each** of the following pieces of information:

- 60 vehicles entered the settlement between 15.00 and 16.00 hours
- 240 vehicles left the settlement between 17.00 and 18.00 hours
- 80 vehicles entered the settlement beween 18.00 and 19.00 hours

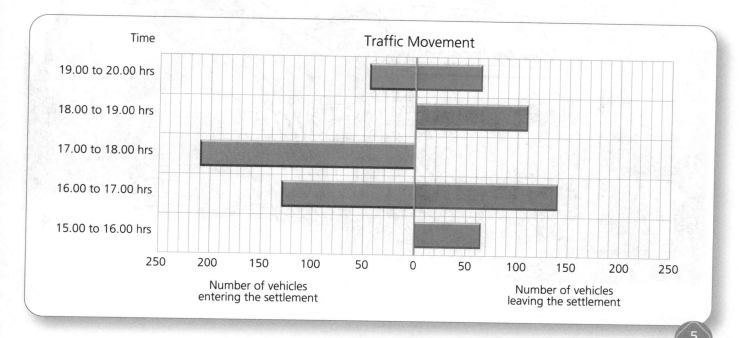

(b) What was the hour of peak traffic flow in the settlement referred to in Figure 5?

_____

(c) Suggest why the hour identified in (b) above was the hour of peak traffic flow.

_____

_____

(d) Calculate the total number of vehicles that entered and left the settlement between 15.00 hours and 17.00 hours.

_____

1

1 The statement that best describes the situation in the cartoon in Figure 1 is:

more land is needed for agriculture ☐

urban development is carefully planned ☐

urban development rolls on at the expense of farmland ☐

suburban housing estates are located at the edge of cities ☐

2 Urban sprawl is:

the spread of a city into the surrounding countryside ☐

a rapid increase in the number of tall buildings in a city ☐

the growth of a city's traffic ☐

the fast growth of a city's population ☐

3 Describe two problems resulting from urban sprawl.

(a) _____

_____

_____

_____

(b) _____

_____

_____

4 Living in a city can offer many advantages. Name three of these advantages.

• _____

• _____

• _____

5 The table in Figure 2 shows crime rates in some Irish counties. Use the table to complete the graph in Figure 3.

COUNTY	Crimes per 1000 population
Carlow	12
Cork	22
Clare	7
Laois	8
Limerick	23
Sligo	13
Tipperary	10
Waterford	10
Wexford	15

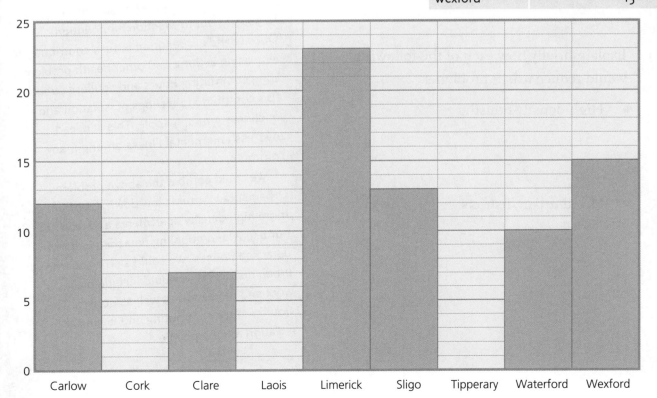

Comprehension and learning exercise

6 Read the news article in Figure 4. Then answer the questions below.

(a) The following are definitions of terms used in Figure 4. Write each term in the space provided.

DEFINITION	TERM:
(i) Residential areas, sometimes at the edges of cities:	
(ii) People who travel to and from work in the city each day:	
(iii) Urban growth over a large area.	

(b) Explain briefly how the rapid growth of Dublin contributes to the following problems:

● Obesity _____

_____

_____

● Loneliness _____

_____

_____

(c) Explain briefly how each of the following would reduce urban problems:

● High-density housing _____

_____

_____

● Mixed urban districts _____

_____

_____

Sprawling Dublin

Fears were expressed in 2007 that if the outward growth of Dublin did not slow down, our capital would by 2050 become as spread-out as Los Angeles, USA – a city notorious for its vast urban sprawl.

The alarming growth of Dublin has created serious problems. People spend longer and longer in their cars commuting to and from ever more distant suburbs. Because they spend so long in their cars, many commuters no longer get enough exercise. This leads to obesity, not to mention air pollution. Obesity and air pollution in turn contribute to increasing asthma and other health problems. Long commuting hours and soulless suburbs also contribute to feelings of isolation and loneliness among people. This can lead to stress and mental illness among many commuters.

We could combat the above problems. Urban sprawl would slow down if we built more high-density apartments and fewer of our usual land-gobbling detached and semi-detached houses. We could also create mixed urban districts that would include places of work and recreation as well as houses. This would reduce commuting and feelings of isolation among people.

1 Indicate whether each of the following statements is true or false by circling the *True* or *False* option:

- Urban renewal entails the restoring or replacing of dwellings and the improvement of facilities for existing inner city communities. *True / False*

- Fatima Mansions in Dublin and the Elysian project in Cork are each examples of urban redevelopment. *True / False*

- Tallaght, Shannon and Craigavon are all examples of new towns that help prevent urban sprawl. *True / False*

2 In the boxes provided, match each of the letters in Column X with the number of its pair in Column Y. One match has been made for you.

COLUMN X			COLUMN Y			
A	Urban sprawl	1	An area of highly skilled workers		A	
B	CBD	2	People who occupy homes illegally		B	
C	Squatters	3	Old buildings replaced by modern structures		C	2
D	Urban renewal	4	Unplanned growth of a city		D	

3 Link each of the letters in Column X with its matching number in Column Y.

COLUMN X			COLUMN Y			
A	Inner city housing areas converted to office blocks	1	Tallaght		A	
B	Inner city houses refurbished for existing families	2	Greenhills		B	
C	Fatima Mansions	3	Examples of 'new towns'		C	
D	Tramway service in Dublin	4	Urban renewal		D	
E	Blanchardstown and Shannon	5	Urban redevelopment		E	
F	An industrial estate in Tallaght	6	Luas		F	
G	Built to house Dublin's 'overspill' city population	7	A renewed area in Dublin		G	

Junior Certificate Higher Level Question with Marking Scheme

4 *'Urban renewal, urban redevelopment and new towns are all used by planners to reduce problems of modern city life.'*

(a) Examine the newspaper extract provided here and state whether it refers to urban renewal or to urban redevelopment.

Newspaper Extract:
Dublin Corporation is trying to persuade people in parts of the old Liberties area of the inner city not to abandon their old neighbourhoods. With this in mind, many houses are being restored by the Corporation and new community services are being provided in the area.

(b) Briefly describe one difference between urban renewal and urban redevelopment.

Marking Scheme
(a) Name correct option = *2 marks*
(b) Make one statement about renewal (*2 marks*) and one statement about redevelopment (*2 marks*) which show the *difference* between them = *4 marks*
(c) Name any new town in Ireland = *2 marks*
(d) Two descriptions at *2 marks* each = *4 marks*
(e) Two problems named at *1 mark* each = *2 marks*

(c) Name any new town in Ireland.

(d) Briefly describe two typical features of this new town.

-
-

(e) Which problems are (i) urban renewal and (ii) new towns designed to reduce?

(i)

(ii)

1 Examine the line graph in Figure 1, which shows population growth in three large Third World cities.

(a) Rank these cities 1, 2 and 3 according to their rates of population growth. (Rank the city with the most rapid population growth as 1.)

_____

_____

_____

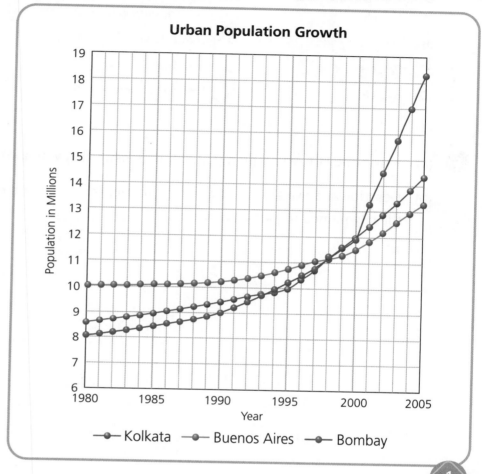

Urban Population Growth

Population in Millions

Year

Kolkata — Buenos Aires — Bombay

(b) In which year did the population of Bombay overtake that of Buenos Aires? _____

2 Indicate whether each of the statements below is true or false by circling the *True* or *False* option.

(a) A **primate city** has at least twice the population of any other city in a country. *True / False*

(b) A **bustee** is a slum area in a city of a developing country. *True / False*

(c) **Commuters** are people who travel long distances to work every day. *True / False*

3 In the boxes provided, match each letter in Column X with the number of its pair in Column Y. One pair has been completed for you.

COLUMN X	
A	Tallaght
B	West of Ireland
C	Polders
D	Bustees

COLUMN Y	
1	Land reclaimed from the sea
2	Shanty towns
3	New town
4	Low population density

A	3
B	
C	
D	

4 (a) Name **one** city with a high population density, that you have studied. _____

(b) Describe and explain two problems experienced as a result of the high population density in the city named in part (a) above.

• _____

_____

_____

_____

_____

_____

_____

• _____

_____

_____

_____

_____

_____

_____

Marking Scheme

(a) One city named = *2 marks*

(b) Two problems at *4 marks* each. Allocate each *4 marks* as follows:

• Statement = *2m*

• Development = *1m*

• Second development or specific example = *1m*

Total: *10 marks*

Chapter 42

Word Games for Fun and to Help You Revise
Chapters 35–42

The figure given in brackets after each clue gives the page of your textbook in which the answer to the clue can be found. (Use this only if you have to.)

Clues Down

A   New town north west of Dublin City (282)

B   CBD (287)

Clues Across

1.   University in Paris CBD (288)
2.   Dublin's river (283)
3.   This brought an end to Ireland's parliament in 1800 (285)
4.   High-rise building in Cork (and Dublin) (290)
5.   Norman headquarters: Dublin _____ (283)
6.   Dublin City's largest open area (282)
7.   These Dublin Mansions underwent urban renewal (304)
8.   Famous cathedral in central Paris (288)
9.   Terminal of Dublin's LUAS line (295)
10.   Dublin's suburban railway system (295)
11.   _____ Street, in Cork's inner city (292)
12.   The river that runs through Paris (288)
13.   There may be many factories in this estate (287)
14.   _____ Street, in Dublin's inner city (292)
15.   People who build dwellings on land they do not own (308)
16.   Indian name for a shanty town (307)
17.   Famous art gallery in CBD of Paris (288)
18.   A large green area in Paris is the _____ de Boulogne (289)
19.   These roads might be built around cities (295)
20.   This canal was built through Dublin in Georgian times (284)
21.   Satellite town of Paris (288)
22.   New town near Limerick (305)
23.   Large shopping area (and famous palace) outside the CBD of Paris (288)
24.   Once a village, now a suburb of Dublin (299)
25.   They founded Dublin (283)
26.   Dublin's tramway system (295)
27.   Old name for Kolkata (307)
28.   These Rovers have their football stadium in Tallaght (305)
29.   Kolkata's country (307)
30.   Very large new town on the southwest of Dublin City (305)

1 Fun Activity

Use this diagram to help you decide whether each of the professions listed below is involved in a primary, secondary or tertiary activity.

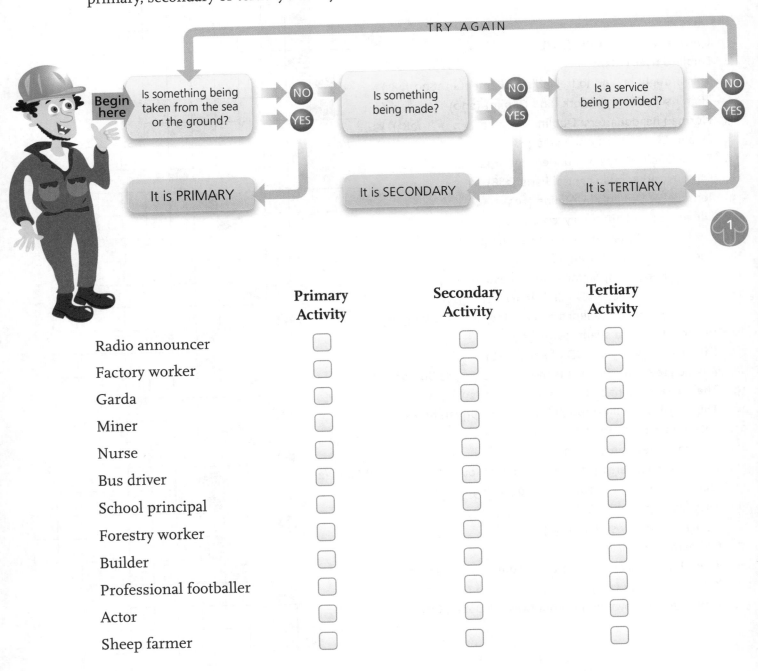

	Primary Activity	Secondary Activity	Tertiary Activity
Radio announcer	☐	☐	☐
Factory worker	☐	☐	☐
Garda	☐	☐	☐
Miner	☐	☐	☐
Nurse	☐	☐	☐
Bus driver	☐	☐	☐
School principal	☐	☐	☐
Forestry worker	☐	☐	☐
Builder	☐	☐	☐
Professional footballer	☐	☐	☐
Actor	☐	☐	☐
Sheep farmer	☐	☐	☐

Tick (✓) the correct box in each case.

Chapter 43

2 Examine each of the photographs labelled **A–C**. Indicate in the spaces provided whether each photograph represents a primary, secondary or tertiary activity.

A _____

B _____

C _____

3 Which of the following groups are all examples of people involved in secondary economic activity?

Dentist, farmer, garda, taxi driver ☐

Teacher, insurance official, nurse, journalist ☐

Bank official, miner, shopkeeper, plumber ☐

Baker, factory worker, cabinet maker, brewer ☐

Tick (✓) the correct box.

4 Examine the OS map of Dungarvan in Figure 2. In the spaces provided, name and give a four-figure grid reference for each of three features that show that people are currently employed in tertiary activities in Dungarvan town.

	FEATURE	GRID REFERENCE
1.		
2.		
3.		

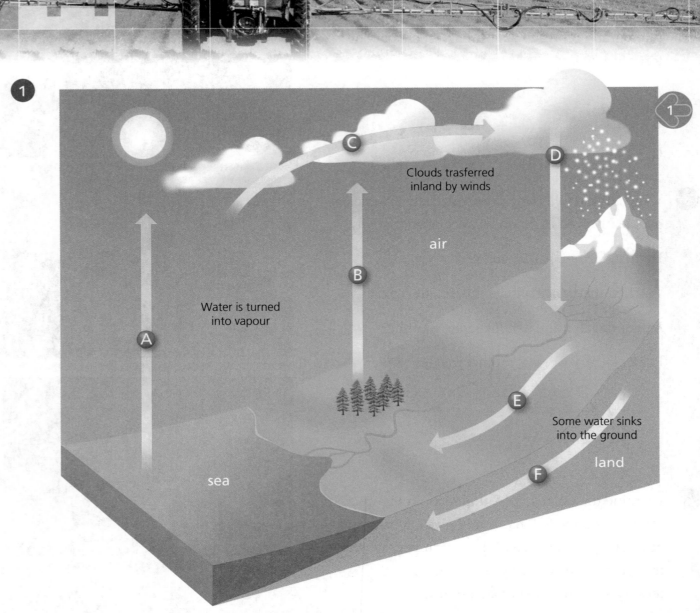

Link each of the labels **A–F** in Figure 1 with its matching statement in *Figure 2*. One match has already been made for you.

LABELS	STATEMENTS
C	**Condensation** – water vapour changes to cloud
	Soakage
	Surface water or **run-off**
	Evaporation from seas, lakes and rivers
	Precipitation – rain, sleet, snow, etc.
	Transpiration from plants

2 With the help of Figures 1 and 2, describe the water cycle. In your answer refer to the terms used Figure 2.

3 **Some ways of conserving water**

Explain briefly how each of the suggestions given in Figure 3 might help to reduce domestic water use.

1

2

3

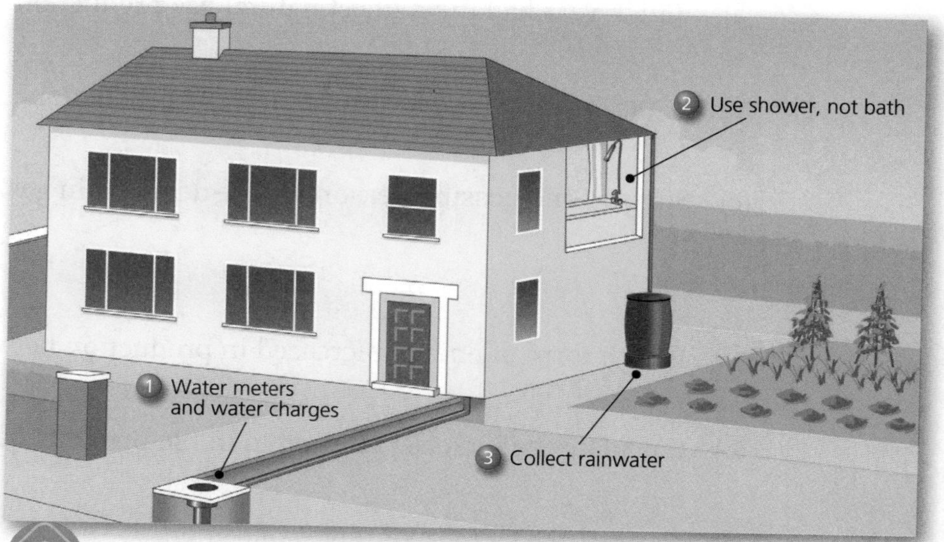

② Use shower, not bath

① Water meters and water charges

③ Collect rainwater

3

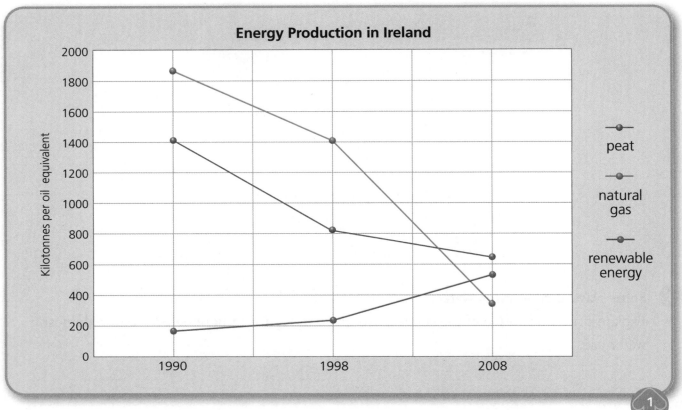

Energy Production in Ireland

(y-axis) Kilotonnes per oil equivalent

peat

natural gas

renewable energy

1 The graph above shows energy production in Ireland for three selected years.

(a) Which year had the highest natural gas production? _____

(b) Which year had the lowest natural gas production? _____

(c) Suggest one possible reason for the decrease in gas production between 1990 and 2008.

_____

(d) Which form of energy increased in production between 1990 and 2008? _____

(e) Calculate the increase referred to in the previous question. _____

(f) Name three sources of renewable energy

• _____   • _____   • _____

Chapter 45

2

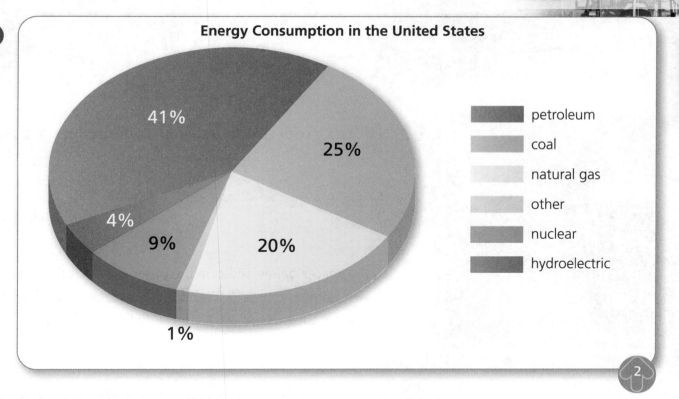

Energy Consumption in the United States

41%

25%

4%

9%

20%

1%

- petroleum
- coal
- natural gas
- other
- nuclear
- hydroelectric

2

Examine the pie chart above showing energy consumption in the United States. Indicate which three statements below are correct by ticking (✓) the three correct boxes.

1. Coal accounts for more than one-third of energy consumption.

2. Petroleum accounts for the largest percentage of energy consumption.

3. Natural gas accounts for the lowest percentage of energy consumption.

4. The percentage of natural gas and nuclear consumption combined is greater than that of coal.

5. Petroleum and natural gas combined account for over 60% of all energy consumption.

   Tick (✓) the three correct boxes:

   1 ☐   2 ☐   3 ☐   4 ☐   5 ☐

3 Describe and explain one positive and one negative effect of a gas or oil discovery in an area.

- **Positive:** _____

  _____

  _____

- **Negative:** _____

  _____

  _____

↑ Transporting milled peat

↑ Cutting a drain in the bog

1 Name each of the machines shown in the pictures **A**, **B** and **C**.

A _____

B _____

C _____

In the spaces below, indicate the order in which the work shown in the pictures **A**, **B** and **C** takes place. Place the letter indicating the earliest work after '1' below and so on.

1. _____   2. _____   3. _____

2 Indicate which **three** of the following statements are correct by placing a tick (✓) after each of the correct statements.

1. Blanket bogs are very deep, up to 10 metres in depth. ☐

2. Raised bogs are mainly found in the midlands. ☐

3. Bord na Móna develops Ireland's peat industry. ☐

4. A grader picks peat from the bog. ☐

5. Peat is a non-renewable source of energy. ☐

3 Explain two reasons why the majority of Bord na Móna's commercial peat production takes place at the raised bogs in the Midlands.

● _____
_____
_____

● _____
_____
_____

Chapter 46

Junior Certificate Higher Level Question with Marking Scheme and Sample Answer

4 (a) *'The use of technology has speeded up the rate of exploitation of Irish peat lands.'*
The diagram in Figure 1 below shows the stages in the exploitation of a bog.
Use the diagram to explain three ways in which technology has been used to exploit the bogs.
(9 marks)

Stage 1	Stage 2	Stage 3	Stage 4
The bog is drained	Peat is harvested	Peat is transported	Peat is marketed

1 Stages in the exploitation of a bog

1 _____

_____

_____

2 _____

_____

_____

_____

3 _____

_____

_____

Marking Scheme
Three explanations each score
3 marks as follows:
- Statement = *2 marks*
- Development = *1 mark*

Sample:
A ditcher digs a network of drains in the bog. **2✓**
These drains allow the bog to become dry enough to work on. **1✓**

(b) *'In the future, Bord na Móna may use cutaway bogs for wind farms.'*
Suggest **three** advantages of cutaway bogs for the location of wind farms. *(6 marks)*
OR
Suggest **three** other ways in which cutaway bogs might be used in the future. *(6 marks)*

1 _____

_____

2 _____

_____

_____

3 _____

_____

Marking Scheme
Three points each score
2 marks as follows:
- Statement = *1 mark*
- Development = *1 mark*

 1 Figure 1 shows figures for the fishing industry in Ireland.

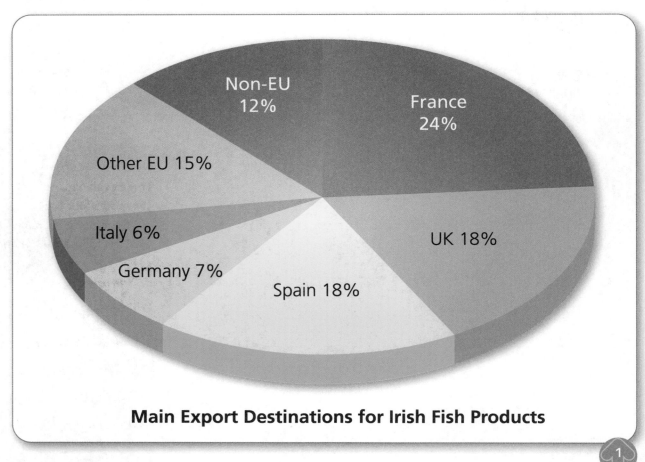

Main Export Destinations for Irish Fish Products

Indicate which of the **three** statements are correct by ticking (✓) the correct box.

1. The largest percentage exported to any one country is 24%.

2. Equal amounts are exported to the UK and Germany.

3. The smallest percentage is exported to Italy.

4. More fish products are exported to non-EU than to other EU countries.

5. Over 50% of fish products are exported to France, Spain and the UK combined.

The correct statements are:

1, 2, 4 ☐   1, 3, 5 ☐   2, 3, 4 ☐   2, 4, 5 ☐

Chapter 47

2 Depletion of a natural resource

Figure 2 shows change over time in herring catches in part of the Celtic Sea off Ireland.

YEAR	ANNUAL CATCH*	YEAR	ANNUAL CATCH*	YEAR	ANNUAL CATCH*
1970	26.7	1980	6.3	1990	12.2
1971	24.9	1981	6.4	1991	11.9
1972	23.4	1982	6.8	1992	13.7
1973	22.6	1983	7.1	1993	10.4
1974	19.3	1984	7.5	1994	8.2
1975	17.2	1985	7.9	1995	7.6
1976	13.6	1986	10.0	1996	6.2
1977	11.0	1987	11.7	1997	6.0
1978	10.7	1988	12.0	1998	6.5
1979	6.7	1989	11.0	1999	6.6

Catch given in thousands of tonnes

 (a) To what extent does the table of figures in Figure 2 show that fish stocks have been depleted over time in part of the Celtic Sea? (*6 marks*)

_____

_____

_____

_____

_____

_____

_____

Marking Scheme

(a) ● Statement = *2 marks*
   ● Reference to a year and catch to support statement = *2 marks*
   ● Reference to another year and catch to support statement = *2 marks*

(b) Three reasons at *2 marks* each. Allocate each *2 marks* as follows:
   ● Statement = *1 mark*
   ● Development = *1 mark*

Write one extra development for each reason.

(b) Describe three reasons for the depletion of fish stocks in Irish waters. (*6 marks*)

   ● _____

   _____

   ● _____

   _____

   ● _____

1 Figure 1 shows production in a mixed farm in Leinster. Examine Figure 1 and answer the questions that follow.

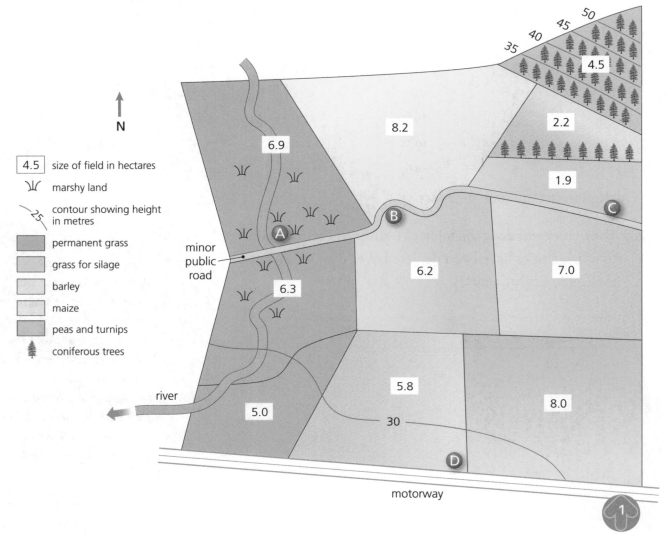

4.5	size of field in hectares
〜	marshy land
25	contour showing height in metres
	permanent grass
	grass for silage
	barley
	maize
	peas and turnips
	coniferous trees

(a) What is the size in hectares of the largest field on the farm? _____

(b) How many hectares are devoted to each of the following land uses?

● **Permanent grass** _____

● **Barley** _____

(c) Of the tillage crops shown, which takes up most land? _____

(d) The pie chart in Figure 2 shows the **percentage** of land taken up by each of the crops on the farm in Figure 1. In the box provided, write the percentage of land taken up by coniferous trees.

 (e) Why is growing coniferous trees a suitable land use for the 4.5 hectare field in the north of the farm?

_____

_____

_____

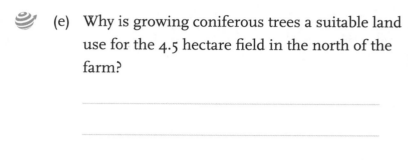

Maize 13%

Barley 24%

Grass for silage 13%

Peas and turnips 13%

Permanent grass 30%

Coniferous trees

2

 (f) A river flows through the farm in Figure 1. In which general direction does it flow?

_____

(g) Imagine that it is proposed to build a farmhouse on this farm at one of the four locations labelled **A** to **D** in Figure 1.

(i) Identify which of the four locations you would choose. _____

(ii) For each of the **other** three locations, state one reason why you would not choose that location to build a farmhouse.

● _____

● _____

● _____

(h) The total size of this farm in hectares (ha) is:

45.7 ha ☐

62.0 ha ☐   *Tick (✓) the correct box.*

67.2 ha ☐

73.0 ha ☐

 (i) Using your answer to question (h) above, calculate the **percentage** of the total farm that is taken up by the field of 6.2 hectares.

_____

2 Tick the boxes provided to indicate whether each of the items listed below is a farm imput, a farm process or a farm output. Some items might be inputs **and** outputs.

	Input	Process	Output
• Tractor	☐	☐	☐
• Ploughing	☐	☐	☐
• Milk	☐	☐	☐
• Cutting silage	☐	☐	☐
• Silage	☐	☐	☐
• Farm buildings	☐	☐	☐
• Animal manure	☐	☐	☐
• EU grants	☐	☐	☐
• Wool	☐	☐	☐
• Keeping farm accounts	☐	☐	☐
• Artificial fertilisers	☐	☐	☐

3 (a) With reference to a farm that you have studied, describe how farming can be described as a system with inputs, processes and outputs.

_____

_____

_____

_____

_____

_____

_____

_____

_____

_____

(b) Explain the term 'mixed farming'. _____

_____

4 Giant Revision Puzzle

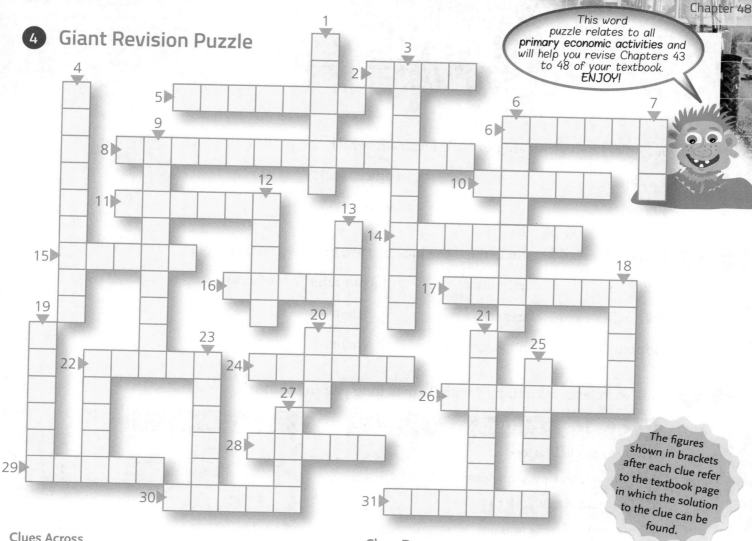

This word puzzle relates to all **primary economic activities** and will help you revise Chapters 43 to 48 of your textbook. **ENJOY!**

The figures shown in brackets after each clue refer to the textbook page in which the solution to the clue can be found.

Clues Across

2. These nets hang like curtains in the water. (338)
5. A primary activity. (316)
6. Another primary activity. (316)
8. Part of the water cycle – rain. (318)
10. Sea between Ireland and Britain. (337)
11. These are part of any system. (341)
14. This machine might be an input in an Irish farm. (341)
15. To give birth. Refers to fish. (338)
16. Equipment used on trawlers to locate other objects. (338)
17. Unusually long period of dry weather. (319)
22. Oil corporation at the centre of the Corrib gas dispute. (326)
24. Saudi _ _ _ _ _ _ _. (324)
26. Money needed to run a farm or any other business. (341)
28. The _ _ _ _ _ cycle. (318)
29. Energy provided by the sun. (318)
30. Something that goes a full circle – as in the water _ _ _ _ _. (318)
31. Machine used to scrape milled peat from a bog. (333)

Clues Down

1. Non-renewable resources are also called this. (323)
3. Process to bring water to dry land. (319)
4. These are part of any system. (341)
6. Oil corporation that developed Kinsale Head Field. (326)
7. Energy source found at Kinsale Head Field. (326)
9. Energy that can be used again and again. (323)
12. Equipment used to locate fish. (338)
13. Gas field off Co. Mayo. (326)
18. Type of net used to scoop fish from near the seabed. (338)
19. Used by EU to limit quantities of fish caught. (339)
20. Isle of _ _ _ is in the Irish Sea. Sounds male.
21. The North _ _ _ _ _ _ _ _ is between Ireland and Scotland.
22. Region on southern margins of the Sahara Desert. (319)
23. River from which South Dublin gets its water supply. (320)
25. A clean and renewable source of energy. (323)
27. This source of power is provided by the sea. (323)

1 **Secondary industries** are normally located in which one of the following:

a garage ☐   an office block ☐

a farm ☐   a factory ☐

2 In the following list, circle the three jobs that are in the secondary sector.

baker   coal miner   computer manufacturer

doctor   farmer   fisherman

shipbuilder   shop assistant   teacher

3 Link each term in column X with its matching pair in column Y.

COLUMN X	
A	Activities in a factory
B	Things with inputs, processes and outputs
C	An input into all Irish factories
D	Outputs of some factories
E	An input into a brewery

COLUMN Y	
1	Electricity
2	By-products
3	Barley
4	Systems
5	Processes

A	
B	
C	
D	
E	

4 Indicate whether the following statements are *True* or *False*.
   (Circle the correct alternative in each case.)

(a) In factories, finished products are processed into raw materials.   *True / False*

(b) Factory buildings, workers and capital are all inputs of factories.   *True / False*

(c) The place where outputs are sold is referred to as 'the market'.   *True / False*

(d) The outputs of some factories can be inputs of other factories.   *True / False*

(e) Intel is a multinational company that has a factory in Leixlip, Co. Kildare. *True / False*

(f) Completed silicon wafers and microprocessors are inputs of the Intel plant. *True / False*

Chapter 49

5 (a) Give the name and location of a factory that you have studied.

_____

(b) Complete the diagram below to show some inputs, processes, outputs and other aspects of the factory you named in (a) above.

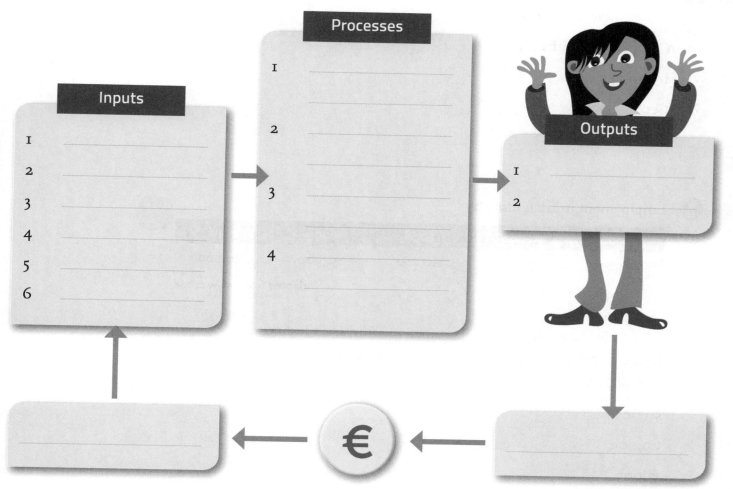

(c) Suggest one local benefit and one benefit to the country of the factory that you named in (a) above.

- **Local benefit:** _____

_____

_____

- **Benefit to the country:** _____

_____

_____

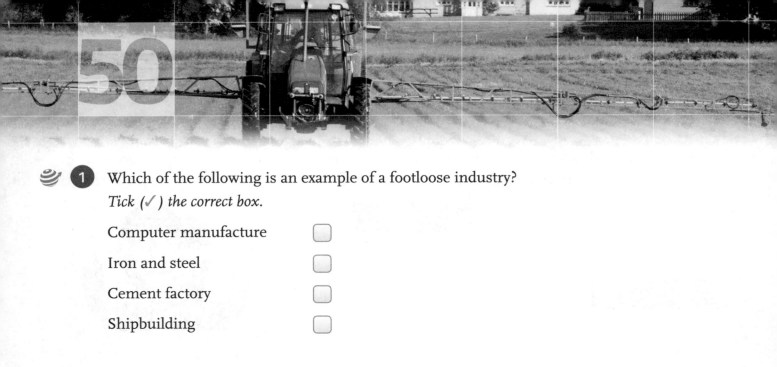

1 Which of the following is an example of a footloose industry?
Tick (✓) the correct box.

Computer manufacture   ☐

Iron and steel   ☐

Cement factory   ☐

Shipbuilding   ☐

2 **Employment in Irish industry**

2006	2007	2008	2009	2010
294,000	299,000	287,000	258,000	240,000

Adapted from www.cso.ie

This table shows the change in employment in Irish industry.
Employment in industry between 2007 and 2010 fell by:
Tick (✓) the correct box.

59,000   ☐

69,000   ☐

53,000   ☐

3 Indicate which three statements below are correct by ticking (✓) the correct box.
1. Modern industries still need to locate near raw materials.
2. Modern industries are footloose industries.
3. Mining is an example of secondary economic activity.
4. Capital is the money used to set up industry.
5. Jobs in the financial sector are an example of tertiary economic activity.

1, 2, 3 ☐   2, 3, 4 ☐   1, 3, 5 ☐   2, 4, 5 ☐

Chapter 50

Junior Certificate question with marking scheme and sample answer

4 **Question:** In relation to a named example of a manufacturing industry you have studied, explain how these three factors have influenced the location of industry: transport; labour and access to raw materials. *(10 marks)*

Marking Scheme

Named industry = *1 mark*

Three factors at *3 marks* each.

Allocate each *3 marks* as follows:

- For transport:
  Statement = *2 marks*
  Development = *1 mark*
- For labour:
  Statement = *2 marks*
  Development = *1 mark*
- For access to raw materials:
  Statement = *2 marks*
  Development = *1 mark*

Sample Answer

Irish Cement of Platin, Drogheda is an example of an industry. ¹✓

1. The factory is located near the M1 Dublin–Northern Ireland motorway. ²✓ This is important because 90% of the factory's products are transported by road. ¹✓

2. Irish Cement employs 200 workers. Most of these come from the nearby town of Drogheda. ²✓ An excellent road network makes it easy for workers to commute to work. ¹✓

3. The factory uses limestone from nearby quarries. ²✓ This raw material is heavy and so it is important for the factory to be near the quarries. ¹✓

10/10

Now answer the same question using **another** named manufacturing industry that you have studied. Use the marking scheme given.

- **Name of industry:** _____

- **Transport:** _____
  _____
  _____

- **Labour:** _____
  _____
  _____

- **Access to raw materials:** _____
  _____
  _____

5 (a) Examine Figure 2. Name **three** ways in
which industry continues to impact on the
environment:

- _____
  _____
  _____

- _____
  _____

- _____
  _____
  _____

(b) Why is industry now less polluting than in
former centuries? Give **two** reasons.

- _____

- _____

Industry and the Environment

Very few industries now pollute the
environment as did the old 'smokestack'
industries of previous centuries. This is
because pollution is now prevented by strict
environmental controls in EU countries such
as Ireland. It is also because most modern
light industries are not of their nature heavy
polluters. But even 'clean' modern industry
is not without some environmental impact.
Heavy traffic to and from factories adds
to road traffic congestion, noise and fossil
fuel emissions that contribute to global
warming. Industrial waste water emissions,
though strictly controlled, may occasionally
break anti-pollution regulations. Some large
factories, such as oil refineries, may also
contribute to visual pollution, especially if
located in picturesque areas.

In newly industrialised countries, pollution
problems are often much more serious than
in Ireland. The Chinese city of Benxi, for
example, is now so polluted with smoke that
it is often invisible to satellites.

Dragons' Den Activity

- Students work in pairs.
- Each pair chooses a type of industry that they would start up in their local
  area. They prepare a ninety-second presentation that will identify the type of
  industry they have chosen, identify its exact proposed location and justify
  their choice on the basis of at least three of the factors that influence the
  location of industry. Student pairs might be given some days to
  prepare this presentation.
- On the day of 'Dragons' Den', each pair will deliver their presentation in
  an attempt to 'sell' their industry to 'the Dragons', who are the other class
  members. It is better if both students take part in the presentation.
- After each presentation, each 'Dragon' rejects or accepts the proposal by a
  show of hands.
- The pair who gets the most acceptances wins.

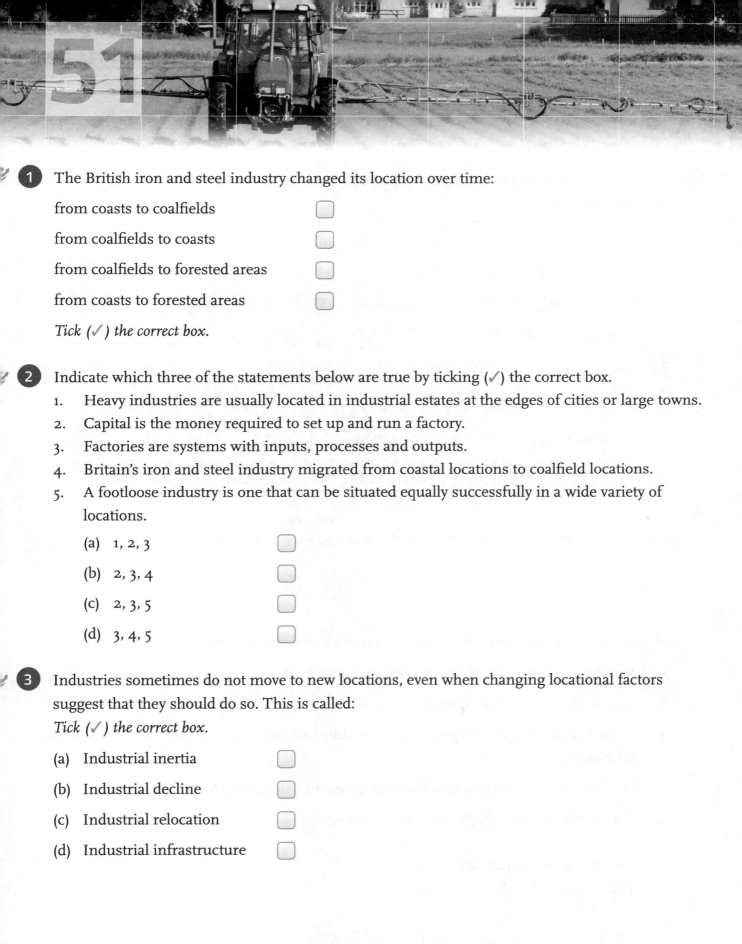

51

1 The British iron and steel industry changed its location over time:

from coasts to coalfields ☐

from coalfields to coasts ☐

from coalfields to forested areas ☐

from coasts to forested areas ☐

Tick (✓) the correct box.

2 Indicate which three of the statements below are true by ticking (✓) the correct box.

1. Heavy industries are usually located in industrial estates at the edges of cities or large towns.
2. Capital is the money required to set up and run a factory.
3. Factories are systems with inputs, processes and outputs.
4. Britain's iron and steel industry migrated from coastal locations to coalfield locations.
5. A footloose industry is one that can be situated equally successfully in a wide variety of locations.

    (a) 1, 2, 3 ☐

    (b) 2, 3, 4 ☐

    (c) 2, 3, 5 ☐

    (d) 3, 4, 5 ☐

3 Industries sometimes do not move to new locations, even when changing locational factors suggest that they should do so. This is called:

Tick (✓) the correct box.

(a) Industrial inertia ☐

(b) Industrial decline ☐

(c) Industrial relocation ☐

(d) Industrial infrastructure ☐

1 The diagram shows the percentages of positions occupied by men and women in a factory in Northern Europe.

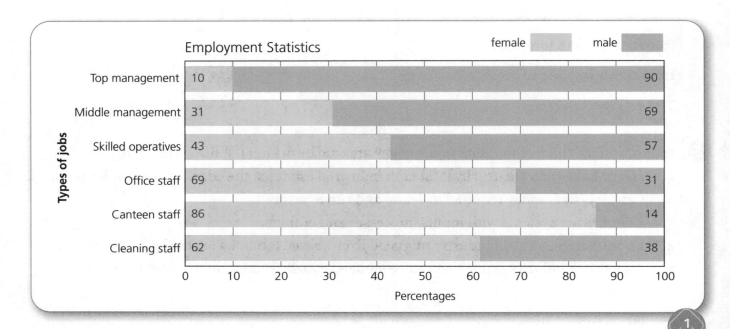

Employment Statistics

female ▢ male ▢

Types of jobs	female	male
Top management	10	90
Middle management	31	69
Skilled operatives	43	57
Office staff	69	31
Canteen staff	86	14
Cleaning staff	62	38

Percentages

Use the graph to indicate which of the statements that follow are true.

1. Men occupy most middle and top management positions.

2. One-third of skilled operatives are women.

3. There is a greater percentage of men in middle management than there is of women among the office staff.

4. For every male canteen worker there are more than three female canteen workers.

5. Most of the lower-paid jobs are done by women.

The correct statements are:
Tick (✓) the correct box.

1, 2, 5 ▢   2, 3, 4 ▢   1, 4, 5 ▢   2, 4, 5 ▢

Chapter 52

2 Study the pie charts below and answer the questions that follow.

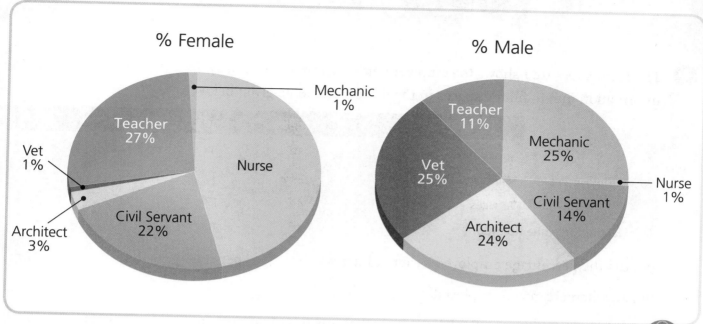

% Female

Teacher 27%

Vet 1%

Architect 3%

Civil Servant 22%

Nurse

Mechanic 1%

% Male

Teacher 11%

Vet 25%

Mechanic 25%

Civil Servant 14%

Architect 24%

Nurse 1%

(a) What percentage of females are nurses in Ireland? _____

(b) Explain **two** of the major differences between the types of jobs that men and women in Ireland have. Give examples from the charts to support your answer.

- _____

  _____

- _____

  _____

3 *The role of women in industry has changed over time.*
Discuss the above statement in relation to Ireland.

_____

_____

_____

_____

_____

_____

1 The table in Figure 1 shows the employment structure for a country. Examine Figure 1 and use the information in it to fill the spaces in the three statements given below.

	SECTOR	1988	1993	2002	2013
% in employment	Agriculture	12	10	7	4
	Manufacturing industry	24	23	21	24
	Services	48	57	63	66
% of labour force unemployed		16	10	9	6

In 2013 the percentage employed in agriculture was _____ per cent.

In 1993 the percentage employed in services was _____ per cent.

In 1988 the percentage of the labour force that was unemployed was _____ per cent.

2 The pie charts labelled **A** and **B** show the percentages of people that work in primary, secondary and tertiary activities in a **developed** country and in a **developing** country.

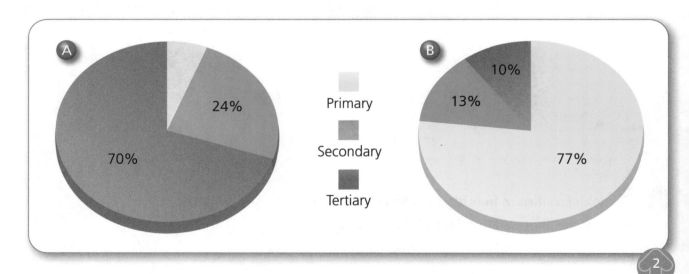

Use the pie charts to answer the questions below.

(a) Calculate the percentage of people who work in primary activities in country A _____.

(b) Which pie chart – A or B – represents the developed country? _____

(c) Which of the following is a developing country: Germany or Mali? _____

1 The flow chart in Figure 1, when complete, will show how acid rain is formed. Select the four **correct statements** from the list given below and place them in the **correct order** to fill each of the blank boxes in Figure 1.

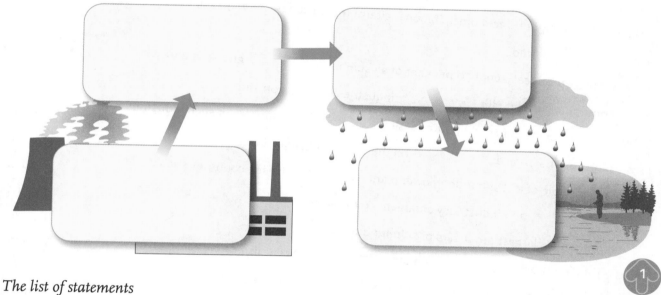

The list of statements

- Precipitation causes the gases to fall as acid rain.
- Motor vehicles, hydroelectric stations, etc. produce fossil fuels.
- The gases evaporate as harmful acid rain.
- Sulphuric oxide and nitric dioxide gases are released into the air.
- The gases combine with moisture and become acids.
- Fossil fuels, such as coal and oil, are burned.
- Sulphur dioxide and nitrogen oxide gases are released.

2 Link each of the terms in column X with its matching pair in column Y.

COLUMN X		COLUMN Y			
A	Have been severely leached by acid rain	1	The Colosseum	A	
B	Is used as a measure of acid rain	2	The United States of America	B	
C	Has had its surface damaged by acid rain	3	Motor vehicles	C	
D	A German area that has been damaged by acid rain	4	pH value	D	
E	Are a major cause of acid rain	5	Soils	E	
F	Is a major producer of acid rain	6	The Black Forest	F	

3

Causes of acid rain

Acid rain is generally caused by the burning of _____ fuels, such as coal, oil and gas. This causes gases called sulphur dioxide and nitrogen oxides to enter the atmosphere. When these gases mix with _____ in the air they are converted into weak _____ and nitric acids which eventually fall as acid rain. A better term to use than acid rain might be acid precipitation – a term that includes not only rain, but also hail, _____ and _____.

- Industry produces about 70 per-cent of all sulphur _____ and so is a major contributor to acid rain. _____ industries such as iron and _____ plants or power plants that burn fossil _____ are examples of such industries. The power station at _____ on the Shannon Estuary in Co. _____ is an example of a coal-burning power plant. Large industrialised countries such as the _____ and industrially emergent countries such as _____ are among the world's largest producers of sulphur dioxide.

- Exhausts from _____ and other motorised vehicles also cause acid precipitation. It is reckoned that exhaust fumes account for 43 per cent of the world's nitrogen _____. These are dangerous gases that can cause illnesses such as _____ among humans. Improved vehicle emissions have now reduced the amount of _____ oxides being emitted per vehicle. But this factor is matched by the fact that more and more cars are being produced throughout the world.

- Our homes also contribute to the production of acid rain. Our _____ or gas central heating; our cosy log fires; even the electricity we use that has been generated from fossil _____ all contribute to acid rain.

- Natural forces, too, cause acid rain. _____ dioxide is generated by _____ eruptions, rotting _____ and – believe it or not – sea spray. But natural forces produce less than 10% of sulphur dioxide and nitrogen oxides. Human activities are responsible for more than _____ per cent of the gases that give us acid _____.

cars
Sulphur
precipitation
USA
sulphuric
fuels
fossil
asthma
Heavy
moisture
ninety
oil
vegetation
oxides
volcanic
sleet
dioxide
Moneypoint
China
nitrogen
steel
snow
Clare
fuel

Use the words in the column below to complete the news extract on the left. Then **learn three causes of acid rain.**

55

1 Conflicts of interest sometimes arise between industrialists and others. Use the spaces provided to outline one example of such a conflict of interest that you have studied.

- **Where** the conflict of interest took place: _____

- The **proposal** that caused the conflict of interest: _____

_____

_____

Two arguments for the proposal	Two arguments against the proposal
1	1
2	2

② Word Puzzle

Enjoy this **revision word puzzle** on manufacturing industry.

The number in brackets after each clue gives the textbook page on which the answer can be found.

Clues Across

2. Coal and oil are examples – two words. (370)
4. The place where industrial outputs are sold. (356)
6. An industrially emergent country in South America. (368)
7. Factor affecting the location of industry – sounds like a political party. (355)
9. Factor affecting industrial location. Could include roads, rail, etc. (355)
10. Location of major steel plant in North-East England. (361)
11. Produced at Teeside and Sheffield. (361)
12. Type of government in China since 1949. (366)
13. EU _ _ _ _ _ _ _ _ _ _ _ Funds have helped to build roads in Ireland. (357)
15. Some factories benefit from these connections with nearby firms. (356)
17. An industry that can be situated successfully in many places. (358)
21. Fine steel is made at this English location. (362)
23. A fossil fuel (370)
24. This Port makes steel in Wales. (361)
25. Acid fog can cause this illness. (371)
26. Special Economic _ _ _ _ _ _ have been set up in China. (367)
27. Acid rain can increase this soil process. (371)

Clues Down

1. Iron _ _ _ is the main resource material for steel making. (360)
3. A factory with extremely bad working conditions. (367)
4. A company with factories in many countries. (352)
5. Activities within a system that turn inputs into outputs. (349)
8. A fossil fuel. (370)
14. The _ _ _ _ _ _ was an ancient centre of iron and steel making in England. (360)
16. Industrial _ _ _ _ _ _ _ _ might discourage a factory from moving to another location. (362)
18. Today's most used fossil fuel. (370)
19. Light industry might be located in an industrial _ _ _ _ _ _ _. (353)
20. River flowing through Drogheda. (357)
22. Industrial Development Authority. (357)

1 All but four of the occupations given in the box relate to tertiary activities.

(a) **Underline** the four activities that are not tertiary activities.

(b) Tourism is an important tertiary activity. **Circle** three activities given in the box that are related to tourism.

> Tour guide, secretary, teacher, nurse, farmer, street cleaner, bar attendant, air pilot, shopkeeper, telesales person, TD, professional footballer, nun, miner, hotel worker, forester, pop star, garda, mechanic, soldier, truck driver, factory worker, judge, bishop, tourist agency worker, accountant

2 The table in Figure 1 below shows the percentages of workers engaged in primary, secondary and tertiary activities in four countries labelled **A–D**. Two of these countries are economically developed and two are economically developing.

(a) Two percentages have been left blank. Calculate and write in these percentages in the blank spaces in the table.

(b) Which two countries are economically developed? How do you know?

- **Economically developed countries:** _____

- **How I know:** _____

  _____

COUNTRY	PRIMARY	SECONDARY	TERTIARY
A	80	12	8
B	4	18	78
C	6	–	79
D	68	20	–

Percentages of workers engaged in primary, secondary and tertiary activities in four countries

1 Tourist numbers

The graph in Figure 1 shows the numbers of tourists who visited a coastal resort in the course of a year.

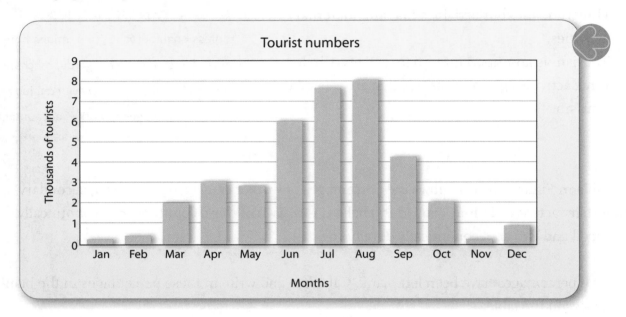

(a) Which is the 'peak' or busiest tourist month at this coastal resort? _____

(b) Using the information in the table in Figure 2 below, explain three reasons why so many people visited the resort during its peak tourist month.

● _____

    _____

● _____

    _____

● _____

    _____

MONTH	J	F	M	A	M	J	J	A	S	O	N	D
Temperature in °C	9	11	13	16	21	25	26	27	19	17	15	12
Precipitation in mm	71	55	28	19	5	5	3	0	6	16	60	79
Daily hours of sunshine	3	4	5	7	9	10	11	11	8	5	4	3

Weather conditions of the coastal resort referral to in Figure 1.

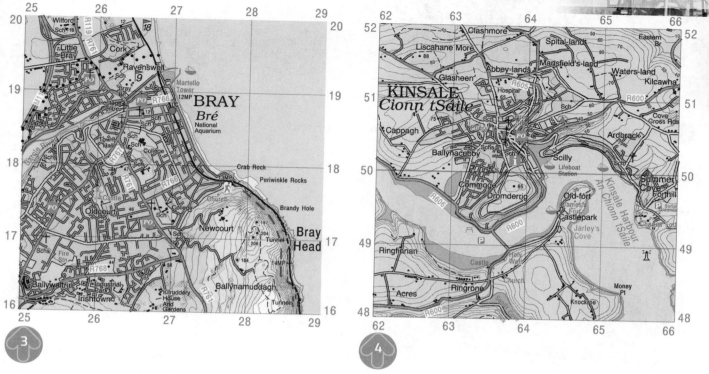

Chapter 57

2 Examine the *OS map fragments above* showing the coastal resorts of Bray (Co. Wicklow) and Kinsale (Co. Cork).

(a) In the boxes below, indicate the presence or absence in each of the resorts of the tourist attractions/facilities listed below.

Attraction/Facility	Bray	Kinsale
● Sandy beach	☑	☒
● Sheltered harbour	☐	☐
● Boating activities	☐	☐
● Campsite	☐	☐
● Youth hostel	☐	☐
● Tourist information	☐	☐
● Antiquities	☐	☐
● Easy access	☐	☐

Place a tick (✓) in the appropriate box to indicate the presence of a facility. Place a cross (✗) to indicate the absence of a facility. One example has been done for you.

(b) In which of the two resorts shown would you prefer to take a holiday? Give one reason for your answer by referring to evidence from the map *only*.

Resort: _____

Why: _____

_____

1 **A** **'Climate makes some regions attractive to tourists.'**

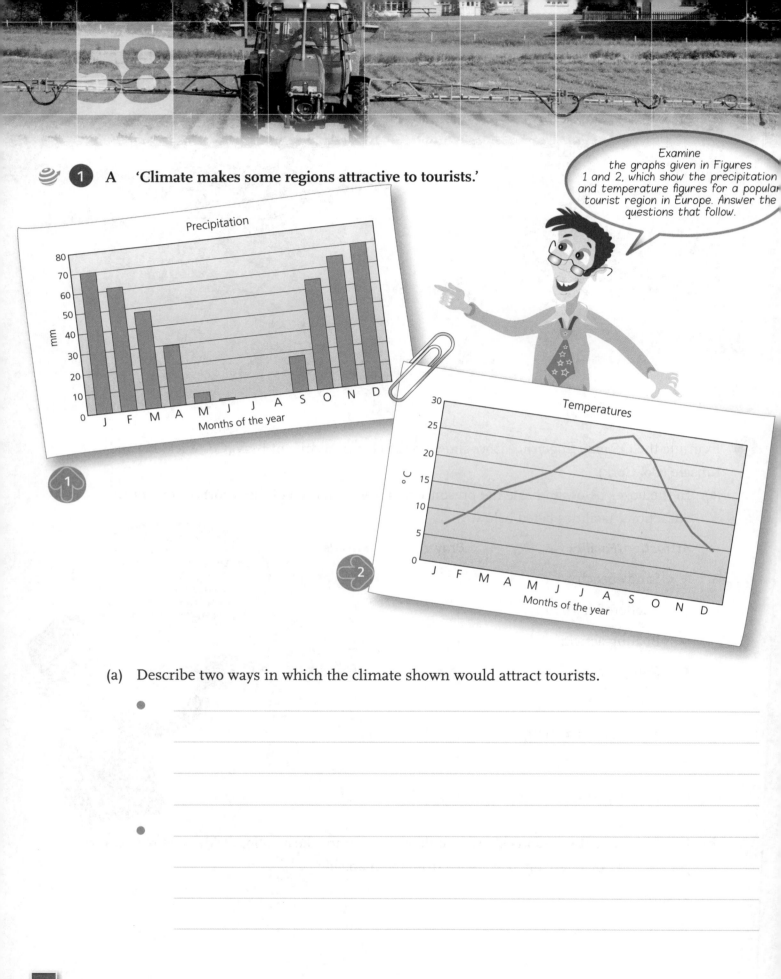

Examine the graphs given in Figures 1 and 2, which show the precipitation and temperature figures for a popular tourist region in Europe. Answer the questions that follow.

Precipitation

Temperatures

(a) Describe two ways in which the climate shown would attract tourists.

(b)   Name the type of climate referred to in Figures 1 and 2 on page 164.

_____

(c)   Name one country in Europe where this type of climate may be found.

_____

B   *'Large-scale tourism can cause major problems for busy tourist regions.'*
Describe **three problems** associated with large-scale tourism.

●   _____
_____
_____
_____

●   _____
_____
_____
_____

●   _____
_____
_____
_____

Marking Scheme

Question A

(a)   Two explanations at *4 marks* each. One explanation must refer to precipitation and the other to temperature.
Allocate each *4 marks* as follows:
  ●   Statement = *2 marks*
  ●   Development referring to graph = *2 marks*
(b)   Name type of climate = *1 mark*
(c)   Name one country = *1 mark*

                                                    Total marks = 10

Question B

Three problems at *4 marks* each. Allocate each *4 marks* as follows:
  ●   Statement = *2 marks*
  ●   Development = *2 marks*

                                                    Total marks = 12

59

1 Which **three** statements best reflects the message of this cartoon?

1. Rich people/countries need to help poor people/nations.

2. It is rude to stare at people while they are eating.

3. Rich people/countries are devouring the world's resources.

4. There are too many poor people in the world.

5. There is great inequality in the world.

6. Rich nations feel that poor nations do not like them.

1, 2, 3 ☐   1, 3, 5 ☐   2, 3, 5 ☐   1, 3, 6 ☐

Tick (✓) the correct box.

	COUNTRY A	COUNTRY B
Primary sector	80	5
Secondary sector	5	25
Tertiary sector	15	70

 The percentages of working people engaged in primary, secondary and tertiary economic activities in two countries

2 (a) Use the statistics in Figure 2 to complete and label the bar graphs in Figure 3.

(b) Use the information in Figure 2 *and/or* Figure 3 to fill in the blanks and to circle the correct alternatives in the passage below.

Country A represents a *slowly developing / developed* country. Its economy is dominated by _____ activities, such as *banking / trading / farming*. Fewest people are engaged in the _____ sector, which employs only *one tenth / one twentieth* of working people. This country could be *China / Uganda*.

Country B represents a *quickly developing / developed* country such as *the USA / India*. Most people in this country work in the _____ sector, which employs *more than / almost* three-quarters of workers. Both _____ and _____ activities are more important in country B than they are in country A. But the _____ sector in country B employs only five per cent of the workforce.

(c) Explain what is meant by 'a quickly developing country'.

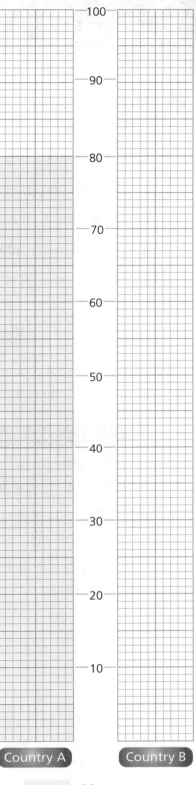

Country A   Country B

☐ Primary sector
☐ Secondary sector
☐ Tertiary sector

1 Impact of Human Activity

Indicate which **three** statements below are correct by ticking (✓) the correct box.

1. Afforestation is the cutting down of forests.

2. Overcropping can mean the growing of the same crops in the same area every year.

3. Desertification has a positive impact on agriculture.

4. Colonialism exploited less well-off countries.

5. Urban renewal is good for inner cities.

1, 3, 4 ☐   1, 4, 5 ☐   2, 3, 5 ☐   2, 4, 5 ☐

2 Link each of the letters in Column X with the matching number in Column Y.

COLUMN X		COLUMN Y			
1	A commodity	A	Brazil	A	
2	Transnational company	B	Crude oil	B	
3	Large farm, usually in the tropics	C	Capital	C	
4	Coffee-exporting country	D	Cash crop	D	
5	Crop grown for money	E	Plantation	E	
6	A type of tax	F	Exports	F	
7	Money used to improve industry	G	Tariff	G	
8	Things sent abroad for sale	H	Nestlé	H	

3 Outline three ways in which First World colonial powers exploited Third World colonies.

1. _____

2. _____

3. _____

Chapter 60

4 The graph shows who makes the profits in coffee production.

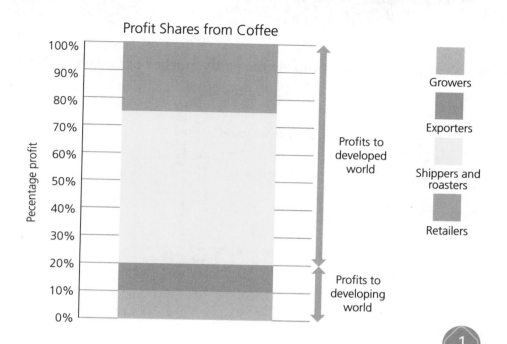

Profit Shares from Coffee

(a) Calculate the percentage profit for each of the four categories shown.

Growers _____ Exporters _____

Shippers and roasters _____ Retailers _____

(b) Explain how unfair trading may be a cause of poverty in the developing world.

_____

_____

_____

_____

_____

_____

_____

_____

_____

_____

_____

1 Use the information in Figure 1 to complete the partly finished bar graph in Figure 2.

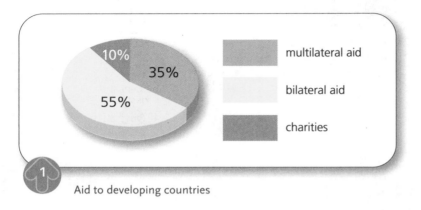

10%

35%

55%

multilateral aid

bilateral aid

charities

1

Aid to developing countries

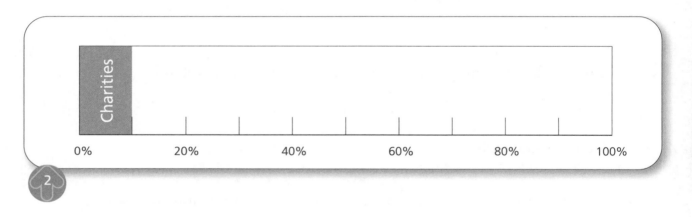

Charities

0%   20%   40%   60%   80%   100%

2

2 In the boxes provided, match each letter in Column X with the number of its pair in Column Y. One pair has been completed for you.

COLUMN X		COLUMN Y			
A	Aid given by the government of Ireland to the government of Ethiopia	1	Bilateral aid	A	
B	Something that is cultivated for sale	2	Tied aid	B	4
C	Aid given through organisations such as the United Nations	3	Emergency aid	C	
D	Medicine, shelter and food	4	Cash crop	D	
E	Aid with conditions attached	5	Multilateral aid	E	
F	An Asian country that receives Irish aid	6	Uganda	F	
G	An African country that receives Irish aid	7	Vietnam	G	

3 The picture below shows the victim of a **tsunami** (huge tidal wave) in Asia.

(a) Describe the type of aid that the person shown in the picture will need immediately. (5 *marks*)

_____

_____

_____

(b) Describe the type of aid that will be needed for future development. (5 *marks*)

_____

_____

_____

Marking Scheme

Allocate each 5 *marks* as follows:

- Statement = *2 marks*
- + development = *2 marks*
- + another development = *1 mark*

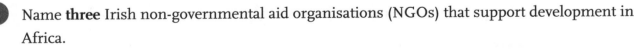 **4** Name **three** Irish non-governmental aid organisations (NGOs) that support development in Africa.

(a) _____

(b) _____

(c) _____

5 **How good are Irish aid programmes?**

Evaluate Irish aid programmes to the Third World. Make four points and mention specific examples of Irish aid.

- _____
- _____
- _____
- _____

6

Which of the following sentences below best matches the message of the cartoon?

The North gives a great deal of aid to the South. ☐

The South is grateful for the aid it gets from the North. ☐

The North takes more money from the South than it gives to the South. ☐

The South is better off because of its relations with the North. ☐

Tick (✓) the correct box.

 1 Explain two ways in which war and the spending of money on arms have prevented economic development in one named developing country of your choice.

(10 marks)

Named country: _____

- **Sample explanation:** *Millions of Sudanese have been killed or injured in civil wars.* ²✓
  Many of the injured people cannot work again. ²✓

- _____
  _____
  _____

- _____
  _____
  _____

2 Which three of the statement below relate best to the message of the cartoon in Figure 1?
Tick (✓) the correct statements

1. Poor people are dreamers. ☐
2. Arms expenditure is hindering development. ☐
3. Military aid is inappropriate aid. ☐
4. Poor people prefer to spend money on arms than on food. ☐
5. People need food, not armies. ☐

Development Snakes and Ladders

(To play and think about.)

Snakes and Ladders game board, squares 1–61:

- 56
- 57 — Unjust world trade
- 58
- 59
- 60 — Famine
- 61 WIN
- 55 — International debt cripples economy
- 54
- 53
- 52 — EU funds new farming scheme
- 51
- 50 — Unclean water causes disease
- 49
- 42
- 43 — Land is redistributed among poor people
- 44
- 45
- 46 — Civil war in Darfur
- 47
- 48
- 41
- 40 — Prices of exports collapse
- 39 — Bilateral aid increases
- 38
- 37
- 36 — Better health education
- 35
- 28 — Foreign banks reduce loan charges
- 29
- 30
- 31
- 32 — Big country invades weaker country
- 33
- 34
- 27
- 26
- 25 — Drought in Sahel
- 24 — Fair trade helps Third World
- 23
- 22 — AIDS kills millions
- 21 — Birth rates fall
- 14
- 15 — United Nations offers help
- 16
- 17
- 18 — 'Military aid' from rich nations
- 19
- 20
- 13
- 12
- 11
- 10
- 9
- 8 — Improved status of women
- 7
- BEGIN 1
- 2
- 3
- 4 — Trócaire sends help
- 5
- 6

53

1 Regional differences

Indicate which **three** statements below are correct by ticking (✓) the correct box.

1. The west of Ireland has a higher density of population than the east.

2. People migrate from the west of Ireland to Dublin.

3. Tertiary activities are well developed in Dublin.

4. Farms in the west of Ireland are generally smaller than farms in the south and east of Ireland.

5. Dublin City has a lower population than Galway City.

1, 2, 3 ☐   1, 3, 5 ☐   2, 3, 4 ☐   2, 4, 5 ☐

2

Indicate whether each of the following statements is true or false by circling the *True / False* option.

(a) The GDA is a developed region in the west of Ireland. *True / False*

(b) The GDA has a total human population of more than 1.5 million. *True / False*

(c) Dublin is Ireland's most important port. *True / False*

(d) The West region earns more than half of all tourist income generated in Ireland. *True / False*

(e) Counties Kildare, Meath and Wicklow are all within the GDA. *True / False*

(f) Milan is the largest city in southern Italy. *True / False*

(g) Rice is an important crop in northern Italy. *True / False*

(h) The south of Italy has Mediterranean-type climate with hot, dry summers. *True / False*

3 Study the map, which shows some richer and poorer regions in Europe.

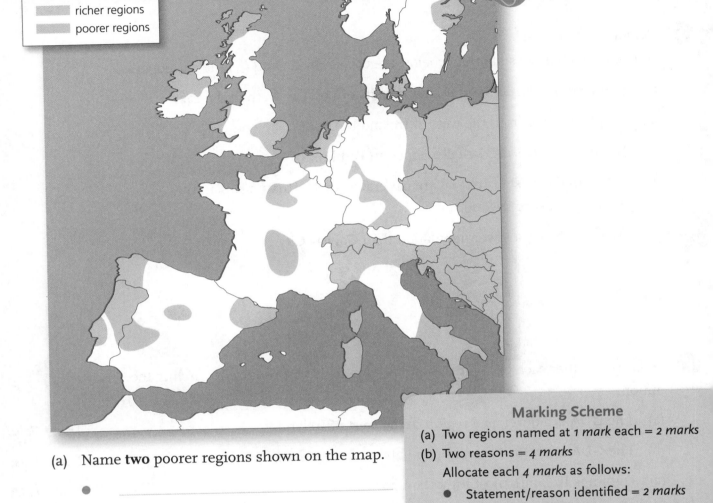

richer regions
poorer regions

(a) Name **two** poorer regions shown on the map.

- _____

- _____

(b) In the case of **one** of the named poorer regions, describe **two** reasons why it is poor.

- _____

_____

_____

_____

- _____

_____

Marking Scheme

(a) Two regions named at *1 mark* each = *2 marks*

(b) Two reasons = *4 marks*
    Allocate each *4 marks* as follows:
    - Statement/reason identified = *2 marks*
    - Two developments at *1 mark* each = *2 mark*

1 Examine the cartoon in Figure 1. Which **three** of the following three statements reflect the message of the cartoon?

1. The world is divided into North and South.

2. The North has given the South a large 'slice' of the world's resources.

3. The good things of the earth are very unevenly distributed.

4. The South has a larger population than the North.

5. There are two men for every one woman in the South.

Tick (✓) the correct box.

1, 2, 3 ☐   1, 3, 4 ☐   1, 3, 5 ☐   3, 4, 5 ☐

2 *'There is great economic inequality between North and South'.*
   (a)   Describe three ways of reducing this economic inequality.

   ● _____

   _____

   _____

- _____

- _____

3 Outline three ways in which Fairtrade helps small coffee producers.

Fairtrade and Gregoria Vargas

Gregoria Vargas is a small coffee grower from Peru. For years she was exploited by multinational companies and greedy middlemen who control the coffee trade. Now an organisation called Fairtrade enables her to earn a living wage with dignity.

Ms Vargas now sells her crop directly to Fairtrade, which treats their growers as partners to be respected, rather than as weak people to be cheated. The organisation pays steady and fair prices to its growers and insists that decent working conditions be provided for all coffee-labourers. It even pays its growers some money in advance, so that they do not have to seek loans from ruthless moneylenders.

You, too, can do your bit for people like Ms Vargas. Look out for the Fairtrade logo and ask for Fairtrade coffee and other Fairtrade products in your local supermarket, café or restaurant. By buying Fairtrade you play a small but important role in reducing inequality in our world.

Google www.fairtrade.ie for short films and other interesting items

- _____

- _____

- _____

Discuss one way in which you and your classmates together might be able to help small-scale coffee producers in the South.